VISUAL IMPAIRMENT; SOCIAL SUPPORT

This book is the fifth in a series published in association with CEDR

Series Editor: *Robin Lovelock*

Already published:

CHANGING PATTERNS OF MENTAL HEALTH CARE
A case study in the development of local services
Jackie Powell and Robin Lovelock

PARTNERSHIP IN PRACTICE
The Children Act 1989
Edited by Ann Buchanan

DISABILITY: BRITAIN IN EUROPE
An evaluation of UK participation in the HELIOS
programme (1988-1991)
Robin Lovelock and Jackie Powell

THE PROBATION SERVICE AND INFORMATION TECHNOLOGY
David Colombi

Forthcoming titles:

WORKLOADS
Measurement and management
Joan Orme

LIVING WITH DISFIGUREMENT
Psycho-social implications of being born with a cleft palate
Poppy Nash

DEMENTIA CARE: KEEPING INTACT AND IN TOUCH
A search for occupational therapy interventions
Cathy Conroy

INFORMATION TECHNOLOGY: IN SICKNESS AND IN HEALTH
A study in the development of computerized nursing records
in a British hospital
Charleen Newton

Visual Impairment; Social Support

Recent research in context

ROBIN LOVELOCK

Avebury
Aldershot•Brookfield USA•Hong Kong•Singapore•Sydney

Published by
Avebury
Ashgate Publishing Limited
Gower House
Croft Road
Aldershot
Hants GU11 3HR
England

Ashgate Publishing Company
Old Post Road
Brookfield
Vermont 05036
USA

British Library Cataloguing in Publication Data

Lovelock, Robin
    Visual Impairment, Social Support:Recent
    Research in Context. - (CEDR Series;
    Vol.5)
    I. Title II. Series
    362.410941

    ISBN 1-85628-391-7

Library of Congress Catalog Card Number: 95--60403

Appendix typeset by Neville Young, 49 Muswell Avenue, London N10 2EH

Printed in Great Britain by
Antony Rowe Ltd, Chippenham, Wiltshire

Contents

PART II THE RESEARCH REVIEWED

PART III FUTURE RESEARCH PRIORITIES

The author

Robin Lovelock is Senior Research Fellow and Director of the Centre for Evaluative and Developmental Research (CEDR) in the Department of Social Work Studies at the University of Southampton. He worked at the Social Services Research and Intelligence Unit (SSRIU), Portsmouth Polytechnic (now University of Portsmouth), from 1974-1988 and was Head of SSRIU from 1983, moving to the University of Southampton in 1988 as Fellow in Applied Social Studies. He has researched and published on social/health care services in a range of areas: physical (including sensory) disability, mental health, provision for elderly people, drug misuse. He has particular interests in the methodology of evaluative research and the role of the social sciences in relation to policy and practice.

Preface

Several important demographic patterns run counter to popular understandings of the nature and incidence of visual impairment. The majority of people with significant sight loss are elderly and are not blind. As well as needs related to their sight problems they typically have other needs, often shared in common with their normally sighted peers.

A recent survey by the Royal National Institute for the Blind (RNIB) (Bruce et al., 1991), building directly upon the more general disability surveys carried out by the Office of Population Censuses and Surveys (OPCS, 1988 and 1989), has suggested that two-thirds of the people in Britain eligible to be registered as blind or partially sighted are aged seventy-five years or over. Only four per cent of those registerable as blind have no light perception whatsoever; the vast majority have varying degrees of residual vision. In addition, progressive deterioration in their sight is the experience of most (eighty-six per cent) visually impaired people, rather than sudden traumatic sight loss (the 'military model') or being severely visually impaired from birth. This divergence in the pattern of onset of visual impairment is also markedly, but not invariably, age-related, as is the patterning of its more specific causes. Similarly, there is a substantial incidence amongst visually impaired people of additional permanent illness or impairment which impacts significantly on their daily lives, again increasing with age.

In 1989 the Department of Health commissioned me to identify and review recent and current research relevant to meeting the social support needs of visually impaired people, and to advise on future research priorities in this area. This book is based on the findings and recommendations of that review. The report presented to the Department in 1991 has been changed as little as possible in preparing it for wider publication over three years later. This Preface seeks to explain and justify this - for it probably does require explanation and justification - and to indicate the ways in which the original text has been amended where not to do so would be misleading or in some other way inappropriate. A Postscript attempts a limited degree of updating with regard to research undertaken since the report was produced, and notes other relevant developments.

The decision to commission the research review was prompted by an awareness within the Department of Health of the demographic patterns outlined on the previous page. This was coupled with a feeling that recent research concerning non-medical help for people with sight loss, including studies which the Department itself had funded, had perhaps been too narrow and over-specialized, reflecting to some extent the inadequate conventional understandings indicated above by concentrating on the mobility problems of people with very restricted vision and the training of specialist workers to assist them. If future research was to inform policy and practice so as to assist the development of more flexible responses to the needs of the client group as a whole, some realignment of research effort might be necessary.

The review deliberately sought to identify systematic work of a research nature carried out by local authorities and voluntary organizations, as well as studies based in academic settings and independent research institutes. To identify future research priorities, the body of research identified was set against the background of the broad policy agenda crystallized in *Caring for People* (DoH, 1989a) and also reflected in a number of recent specialized reports and papers in the visual impairment field (DHSS (SSI), 1988b; DoH, 1989b; DoH (SSI), 1989c).

The report on the review (Lovelock and Edge, 1991) was not widely circulated at the time. This was not because its findings and recommendations were unwelcome to the DoH, but because it was agreed to publish it in book form in the series in which it now appears. The blame for the longer than normal delay in effecting this rests entirely with the present author, whose excuse lies in the pressure of other commitments, not least carrying out further research on the social support of visually impaired people.

Given that the review involved a postal survey and the use of published research indexes, any listing of specific projects in the report was bound to be 'out-of-date' in an obvious sense by the time it appeared. The passage of several more years has clearly exacerbated this; in particular it limits the value as a reference source in the particular field which the Directory as such was originally felt to possess. However, this was a subsidiary concern of the project, and what appears here as an Appendix retains its value as a document of record.

A more substantial ground for thinking that the study as a whole must be 'past its sell-by date', including and in particular the conclusions and broad recommendations based upon it, might be that the policy and practice context had dramatically changed. It will be the implicit burden of the present text as a whole, and the explicit focus of the Postscript, to demonstrate that this is not the case, despite potential and actual changes in the organization and delivery of services since the research was carried out, primarily as a result of implementation of the NHS and Community Care Act 1990.

During the past few years, the ideas of 'the disability movement' have influenced at least the thinking of many able-bodied researchers, practitioners, and policy makers. In my view this is a significant advance, albeit that many would, with justification, comment that in so far as this is indeed the case it is merely a beginning. Several elements of the radical critique of conventional perspectives must be mentioned. One key area which has presented problems in preparing this book, and so demands particular attention here, is the heightened sensitivity now apparent to the implications of the language used in discussing disability issues.

As a basis for understanding and action, 'the social model of disability', as outlined for example by Oliver (1990, 1991), gives priority to the impact of the economic, social and physical barriers of 'disabling environments' upon the daily lives of disabled people. It emphasizes how the discrimination and marginalization involved are experienced in common by disabled people as an overall group. This is contrasted with 'the medical model', which is characterized as focusing on the various losses, limitations, or abnormalities of bodily function manifest in individuals and attempts to cure or ameliorate them.

Many articulate disabled people have drawn on 'the social model' in making sense of their own experiences and providing an important, collective, and cogent critique of the excessively individualistic approaches embedded in conventional services - social as well as medical. A significant element of this is a tendency to categorize disabled people into a variety of sub-groups, such as 'people with a visual impairment'. In this context, critics have pointed to the ways in which what they call 'headcount' statistics - including, in their view, the OPCS, RNIB, and similar surveys - reflect 'the medical model' by framing questions against a background of disability conceived as an individual property *rather than* [this author's emphasis] a social construct (Oliver, 1987, 1990; Abberley, 1991, 1992).

Researchers, not only those who conduct large-scale surveys, but also those who collect the views and experiences of disabled people by more qualitative means and use them for their own purposes, are held - in ways which demand an adequate response - to be implicated in the same disempowering paradigm (see especially the recent Special Issue of *Disability, Handicap & Society* (1992) devoted to 'Researching Disability').

A further dimension of this far-reaching critique of conventionally dominant perspectives and the policies and practices they inform and sustain, is a rejection of the notion of 'care', at least in its paternalistic sense, in favour of emphasizing independence based on rights, enabling, and empowerment (Finkelstein, 1991; Morris, 1993). Self-assessment of disabled people's needs, and peer-counselling, are advocated, instead of assessment and counselling by professionals (see for example the contributions by Sapey and Hewitt, and by d'Aboville in Oliver, 1991).

It is beyond the scope of this book, not least this Preface, to make a sustained and detailed attempt to engage with these important issues, central to current conceptual and political debates around disability policy, practice and research though they are. In focusing specifically upon visual impairment, and on the needs and social support of visually impaired people, and in having made use already of statistical data drawn from large-scale surveys, the author does not wish to be seen to reject the critical perspectives sketched in the preceding paragraphs. The understanding gained in conducting the research reported here, and more particularly the experience of carrying out two subsequent studies, one completed (Lovelock and Powell, 1994) and one current (see Postscript), each of which has involved more direct contact with organizations of and for disabled people, have encouraged considerable sympathy with the views of leading representatives of the disability movement. However, I feel able to endorse 'the social model of disability' as thus far formulated by Oliver (1990, 1991) and others only in a qualified way, at least in an academic rather than a political context, since it seems to me to require rather more careful explication in relation to large issues in social and political theory and in the philosophy of the social sciences than it typically receives. This need not - and cannot - detain us here. I have no doubt that there are many grounds for general and/or detailed criticism of what is written in these pages, although the following summary argument seems to me to justify the approach taken in the present specific context.

Beardshaw (1988) has shown that services for physically disabled people (including people with a sight or hearing impairment) have continued to be given the lowest priority by health and social services amongst the four 'priority groups' identified in *Care in Action* (DHSS, 1981) and now the targets of 'community care'. Accounts of the history of provision for visually impaired people (Abel, 1987, 1989; Phelan, 1984) indicate both persistent uncertainty and fluctuation over time as to how far and in what ways they have been and should be regarded as a special group amongst disabled people. I believe that the material presented and analysed in this book demonstrates the importance of attending to the special situation of people with a visual impairment, whilst keeping in mind the features of their experience shared in common with other disabled people. Statistics are used here simply to point, in the crudest quantitative way, to the general area in which we are interested, and to indicate issues whose real understanding and implications deserve detailed qualitative study, drawing above all on the felt experience of the people concerned.

It must, however, be stated explicitly here that there has been a change in terminology as between the original report on the research review and the present version in book form. In conducting the research itself, and in the original report upon it, the term 'visual *handicap*' (and equivalents) was used to indicate the focus of discussion. 'Visual *impairment*' (and equivalents) has been substituted at all appropriate points in the present text. The original discussion of terms and the argument supporting the use of 'handicap' has been deleted from the main text. An amended version of the earlier discussion, reconsidering the issues and reaching a different conclusion, is offered in the following paragraphs.

Acknowledging 'the confusion over terminology' in the whole field of concern, the OPCS researchers embarking on their *Surveys of Disability in Great Britain* (1988 and 1989), commissioned by the Department of Health, adopted the schema produced by Phillip Wood (1980), which was a development of that used by Amelia Harris in her earlier (1971) national survey. The World Health Organisation had accepted Wood's approach as a basis for classifying illness, disease and disability (WHO, 1981). It is appropriate to quote at length from the detailed discussion by the OPCS authors of what they saw as the main issues (*OPCS Surveys of Disability in Great Britain, Report 1*, pp. 6-8):

> The International Classification of Impairments, Disabilities and Handicaps [ICIDH] identifies three different concepts as consequences of disease and presents a classification for each. They are defined as follows:
>
> *Impairment:* 'Any loss or abnormality of psychological, physiological or anatomical structure or function.' Here we are dealing with parts or systems of the body that do not work.
>
> *Disability:* 'Any restriction or lack (resulting from an impairment) of an ability to perform an activity in the manner or within the range considered normal for a human being.' Here we are talking about things people cannot do.
>
> *Handicap:* 'A disadvantage for a given individual, resulting from an impairment or disability, that limits or prevents the fulfilment of a role (depending on age, sex and social and cultural factors) for that individual.' This is in relation to a particular environment and to relationships with other people.

The OPCS authors also noted that the ICIDH uses the term 'disablement' as the generic term referring to all the consequences of disease, such that 'disablement' embraces all three concepts in the schema. In terms of the inter-relationships of the concepts, disease leads to impairment, which leads to disability, which leads to handicap. However, impairment can also lead to handicap as it were 'directly' or 'without disability', as where disfigurement causes difficulties in social integration.

One example given to illustrate the meanings and inter-relationships of the three concepts, and which is relevant to our concerns here, is as follows:

IMPAIRMENT	DISABILITY	HANDICAP
Vision	Seeing	Orientation

Impaired vision makes it difficult for a person to see and (thence) to orientate her/himself and/or to function effectively within her/his environment.

Adding to the specific complexities of this conceptual framework as regards the particular field of interest of our study:

> In the case of some impairments, such as vision and hearing, there is more or less one-to-one correspondence between impairment and disability if the impairment is sufficiently serious. However, it should be noted that although a large proportion of the population suffer from visual impairment, because of the availability of adequate glasses or contact lenses to correct impaired vision, far fewer people can be said to have a seeing disability.

It should also be noted that, in the terms of this categorization, problems of orientation are not the only handicap(s) resulting from impaired vision.

A final pertinent point made in setting out the conceptual background of the OPCS Surveys is that:

> Elderly people in general are not usually thought of as being disabled, but the above [i.e. the WHO] definition of disability means that it is the old who are most likely to be disabled as the ageing process takes its toll and restricts the activities that [can be performed].

The general framework based upon the WHO definitions is at first sight helpful, for example in delineating the respective concerns of various professions:

> In the field of visual disablement, the [WHO] model suggests that visual impairment is the primary responsibility of ophthalmologists, whose medical training enables them to prevent, cure, or reduce the disorders of the ocular system by surgery or medication. Visual disability also falls within their province or, perhaps more accurately, within the skills area of the ophthalmic opticians who may be able to overcome a permanent, incurable physical abnormality of the eye by prostheses, ie by prescribing correcting lenses or spectacles to counteract aberrations in the eye. However,

when the experts in impairment and disability have done all they can, there may remain for some people a potentially permanent handicap to their personal, social, and vocational development. Responsibility for handling these handicapping consequences will rest with the psychologists, teachers, social workers, and technical and mobility officers, ie within the habilitation and rehabilitation professions. (Tobin, 1984)

In the piece quoted Tobin's focus is:

... research that falls within the general area of non-medical support ... [not] research programmes concerned with the prevention and cure of severe visual impairment. (ibid.)

This distinction was precisely applicable in delineating the boundaries of our review. By association, through drawing on Tobin's self-styled 'cockshy' at identifying research priorities, we explicitly and implicitly employed the WHO terminology, both in seeking to identify relevant research and in reviewing the material collected. The term 'visual handicap' (or similar) was therefore used throughout our report.

Disabled People's International (DPI) opposed the WHO classification from the start. Finkelstein, at the time Chair of its British counterpart, the British Council of Organisations of Disabled People (BCODP), argued in a paper given at a WHO meeting in the Netherlands in June 1985:

I remained [sic] convinced ... that this classification system in its present form reinforces medical and administrative approaches towards us and that in this respect, it is not in our best interests to support it. (Finkelstein, 1985, quoted in Oliver, 1990, p. 6)

Oliver himself endorses the (earlier) two-fold distinction offered by the Union of the Physically Impaired Against Segregation (UPIAS):

Impairment lacking part or all of a limb, or having a defective limb, organism or mechanism of the body;

Disability the disadvantage or restriction of activity caused by a contemporary social organisation which takes no or little account of people who have physical impairments and thus excludes them from the mainstream of social activities. (Oliver, 1990, p. 11; referring to UPIAS, 1976, pp. 3-4)

It is indicative of the influence which these ideas have had, particularly during the last ten years, that a recent publication from the Social Services Inspectorate (DoH (SSI), 1993, p. 36) adopts the following definitions:

Impairment lacking part, or all, of a limb, or having a defective organism[1] or mechanism of the body;

Disability the loss or limitation of opportunities to take part in the normal life of the community on an equal level with others due to cultural, physical and/or social barriers.

It is, I believe, evident that the delineation of our subject matter with reference to Tobin's paper (see quotations on preceding pages), as essentially non-medical, and concerning the work of 'the habilitation and rehabilitation professions' rather than those 'concerned with the prevention and cure of severe visual impairment', neither depends upon nor entails the three-fold WHO categorization. In this book therefore, the terms 'visual impairment', 'visually impaired people', 'people with a visual impairment' etc. have been used, in recognition of the appropriately increased sensitivity in the years since our review was carried out to what, in discussing precisely these definitions of disability, Oliver (1990) calls 'the politics of meaning', and to reflect broad agreement with the reasons for rejecting the term 'handicap'. Certain unavoidable exceptions to this general rule are discussed in the next paragraph.

By convention, quotations from other writers appear in their original form. Likewise, neither the titles of projects, nor direct quotations from material supplied about them, whether in the main text or in the Directory which features as a substantial Appendix to this book, have been amended. Superficial as such shifts in linguistic usage may be, the changing conventions already referred to suggest that if the exercise were to be repeated now, smaller proportions of the projects identified would have titles containing words and phrases such as 'handicapped', 'the blind' and so on than was the case when we carried out our review.

One straightforward change made to the text of the original report in preparing this book is in the order in which the presentation and discussion of the material collated and the development of recommendations for future research appear; similarly the location of the Directory has been altered.

A more consequential modification is the addition at certain points either of brief author's comments (in brackets) or of numbered notes, where not to alert readers 'immediately' - i.e. rather than via the Postscript - to subsequent changes, or not to supply additional information, would be misleading. Where notes are used these are referenced in the main text using superscript, with all such notes in a particular chapter collected at the end of that chapter.

The final significant change to the text of the report submitted to the Department of Health in 1991 concerns what here constitutes the concluding chapter of the main text (i.e. Chapter 7), the style of which reflects a slight broadening of the frame of reference in discussing the future research agenda. As commissioners of the review, the Department constituted the initial audience for the report upon it. Our recommendations were, however, always conceived as being addressed to a wider community of interest, and this has been accentuated in this book.

The several caveats, reinterpretations, and editorial devices to which attention has been drawn in this Preface, complemented by the specific attempt in a Postscript to give some account of more recent research developments, constitute the author's best efforts to preserve as far as possible the integrity of the original text of the report on the 1989-91 review, whilst providing sufficient updating to make this book a valid contribution at the present time.

The least tractable difficulty caused by the passage of time since the review was carried out remains. It is that a major organizing dimension of the material collected was whether a project had been completed or was still current at the time information was supplied. It is a reasonable assumption that all of the projects included in the Directory have by now either been completed or aborted - unless of course the stated end-date has not yet been reached. No attempt at full and systematic updating has been made. At the very least this would have involved collecting additional information on projects listed at the time as 'ongoing'; more substantially, one could have sought to identify all subsequent (including current) work relevant to the concerns of this book. Any of this would have been to embark upon a considerable additional research task, for which resources have simply not been available.

The justification for including in this book what, despite the foregoing discussion and the modifications indicated and grounded in it, is admittedly now dated and incomplete material (i.e. the Directory itself) is two-fold. The research priorities identified in the original report remain substantially valid, albeit that the discussion in which they are now presented takes a slightly modified form. The case for arguing that this is so is made in the Postscript to the main text, which includes a necessarily superficial survey of subsequent research. The original recommendations for future research were based directly upon an analytical account of the projects identified during the 1989-91 review, which must therefore be presented along with them. Also included in the Postscript is information about research in which the author is currently involved, which directly addresses the main priorities identified through the review.

Notes

1   'Organism' - as opposed to 'organ' perhaps - seems rather odd in this context. However, as the immediately preceding quotation in the text reveals, this was the term employed in the earlier UPIAS definition of impairment (as quoted by Oliver, 1990), which it is assumed has influenced the recent SSI formulation.

Acknowledgements

Thanks are due to a considerable number of people, for contributing in various ways to the original research review and/or for help and support during the extended period over which - in fits and starts - this book has been in preparation.

Sally Edge, whose research and practice experience concerning visual impairment were invaluable, edited and collated returns from our postal survey, carried out library searches, and with me visited the major research centres. From the range of material received she produced the initial drafts of the essay which was at the heart of the original review and which now, with further modification, appears as Part II of this book. She also drafted parts of the brief historical account which appears here in Chapter 1, and contributed to the original version of the discussion of future research priorities which remains the basis of Part III of the present text. Jo-Anne Ireland, CEDR Secretary at the time, created a database of projects and entered the edited contents of the returns, as well as carrying out a host of other secretarial tasks with typically unfailing good humour. With further editorial work by Sally Edge and myself that database became a Directory of Projects in the original report. Neville Young's typesetting skills have enabled this to be incorporated in this book as an Appendix.

Thanks go to the Department of Health for commissioning and funding what proved to be a very stimulating project, as well as a more substantial one than perhaps any of us thought at the outset. Hazel Canter, Madeleine Simms, and Eleanor Grey were our successive Research Liaison Officers. Eleanor saw the review through to conclusion and her support was greatly appreciated. Also within the Department of Health, discussions with Mary Jobbins (SSI), Judith Liebling and Dr Annette Rawson, and their comments on an interim report, were immensely helpful. The Department also made a financial contribution towards the revision of the material for publication in book form. The opinions expressed are, however, those of the author and not of the Department of Health.

Without the efforts of everyone who completed our *pro formas* - including 'nil returns' - and who sent reports on studies and/or other material, the original report, and ultimately this book, could not have been produced. Special thanks must be expressed to Allan Dodds and his colleagues at the Blind Mobility Research Unit at the University of Nottingham and to Michael Tobin at the Research Centre for the Education of the Visually Handicapped, University of Birmingham, not only for their substantial direct contributions of material, but for their hospitality on our visits and for valuable discussions both face-to-face and on the telephone. For this book, Allan and Michael each also responded willingly to my request for a brief update on the more recent work of BMRU and RCEVH respectively, as did Graham Willetts of RNIB's Social Services Development Unit in respect of his and colleagues' work. The earlier help of a number of other staff of the RNIB must also be acknowledged here, as should the considered reflections of Patrick Phelan and Hazel Osborn on some of the professional issues involved.

My colleague Jackie Powell has provided help and support in a variety of ways over an extended period. First, through a series of discussions, she made a significant contribution to the argument which structured the discussion of research priorities in the original report. She also made constructively critical comments on successive drafts of the other elements of that document. More recently, she has been a constant source of help in the restructuring of the original report as the basis of this book. She has sustained my commitment to the project when it has threatened to evaporate - whilst also ensuring that other research in which we have been jointly engaged meanwhile has not been entirely ignored!

My final set of thanks go to Jo Gooderham, Suzanne Evins and Pat Marks at Avebury, for their understanding and support during the preparation of this text and for their continuing help with the CEDR Series. I have come to take Jo's patience for granted - in the best sense I hope. It has reached new heights with each revised date for the delivery of this typescript.

Robin Lovelock
Southampton, December 1994

List of abbreviations

ACC	Association of County Councils
ADSS	Association of Directors of Social Services
AMA	Association of Metropolitan Authorities
BCODP	British Council of Organisations of Disabled People
BMRU	Blind Mobility Research Unit (University of Nottingham)
BRSB	Bristol Royal Society for the Blind
CCETSW	Central Council for Education and Training in Social Work
CQSW	Certificate of Qualification in Social Work
CSO	Central Statistical Office
DBSLG	Deaf-Blind Services Liaison Group
DoH	Department of Health
DHA	District Health Authority
DHSS	Department of Health and Social Security
DPI	Disabled People's International
DipSw	Diploma in Social Work
ESRC	Economic and Social Research Council
FPC	Family Practitioner Committee (now Family Health Services Authority (FHSA))
GDBA	Guide Dogs for the Blind Association
HACB	Hampshire Association for the Care of the Blind
ICIDH	International Classification of Impairments, Disabilities and Handicaps
LA(s)	Local Authority(ies)
MRC	Medical Research Council

MSC	Manpower Services Commission
NDBL	National Deaf-Blind League
NFER	National Foundation for Educational Research
NHSME	National Health Service Management Executive
NMC	National Mobility Centre
NRAB	North Regional Association for the Blind
NVQ	National Vocational Qualifications
OPCS	Office of Population Censuses and Surveys
PHRRC	Public Health Research and Resource Centre (Salford)
PSS	Partially Sighted Society
RCEVH	Research Centre for the Education of the Visually Handicapped (University of Birmingham)
REACH	Retired Executives Action Clearing House
RHA	Regional Health Authority
RNIB	Royal National Institute for the Blind
RNID	Royal National Institute for Deaf People
SENSE	National Deaf-Blind and Rubella Association
SRAB	South Region Association for the Blind
SSD	Social Services Department
SSI	Social Services Inspectorate (Department of Health)
SSRG	Social Services Research Group
SWSG	Social Work Services Group (Scottish Office, Home and Health Department)
UPIAS	Union of the Physically Impaired Against Segregation
WHO	World Health Organisation
WRVS	Womens Royal Voluntary Service

Introduction

As indicated in the Preface, towards the end of the 1980s a feeling had grown within the relevant sections of the Department of Health that recent research concerning the social support of people with impaired vision, including that funded by the Department itself, had not adequately reflected the implications of accumulating evidence concerning the main characteristics and needs of the target client group.

In particular, it was felt that future applied research in this field should acknowledge two inter-related understandings. Firstly, the majority of people with sight problems are not, in fact, totally blind, but rather have varying degrees of low vision. Secondly, a large majority of these people are elderly, and may have a variety of other social care needs, many of them common to their normally sighted peers. Viewed against this background, a good deal of recent research, although valuable, was felt to have been somewhat narrowly focused and, in an important sense, over-specialized. As we came to see in more detail, there had been a major pre-occupation, not least in the Department's own programme, with research on mobility, mobility training, and the training of specialist workers to provide mobility and, to a lesser extent, other rehabilitative training.

In consequence, it was felt that the Department's research programme in this area should be realigned, so as to better reflect the broad spectrum of needs relevant to the client group(s) concerned, giving greater attention than hitherto to questions around appropriate provision, service organization, delivery, and funding. To inform the necessary rethinking, a review of recent and current research relevant to the social support of visually impaired people was commissioned. Such a review, whilst primarily for the Department of Health, might also provide a means to influence the wider community of researchers and research funding bodies in similar directions, thereby encouraging a common effort.

The formal brief for this work required the identification of relevant recent and current research, the production of a comprehensive and structured listing of studies, and the preparation of an analytic account of their subject matter and general findings, identifying significant gaps and thereby developing a framework for future research. This book is based on the work carried out to meet the terms of this brief during 1989-91. The measures taken to reflect the subsequent passage of time in preparing this text for wider publication several years later are indicated in the Preface.

The main body of the book is in three parts. Part I contains two short chapters. The first offers a brief historical and conceptual introduction to the field of visual impairment, then discusses in some detail the background and context of the research review. Chapter 2 sets out the formal aims of the study, going on to describe the general methodological approach taken to identifying relevant projects for inclusion. It concludes with a discussion of the rationale for the organization into sections and sub-sections of the Directory which lists the projects on which details were collected. The Directory itself constitutes a substantial Appendix. It contains sixty-nine individual entries, preceded by a list of the projects included, in the order in which they appear. Two additional indexes follow the project entries. The first groups and lists (alphabetically within the groups) the organizations responsible for one or more studies; the second simply lists all projects alphabetically by title.

Part II presents in a structured way the body of work listed in the Appendix. A brief introduction contains some general observations about the overall body of material and explains the structuring of the discussion into the three chapters which follow. What is offered is not conceived as a thorough review of the research literature, although the discussion draws together and summarizes the subject matter and general findings of the studies collated.

Part III attempts to locate the overall body of research identified in the current policy context, with particular attention to the themes making up what may be termed 'the community care agenda'. This generates a framework within which to make recommendations concerning future research priorities.

A Postscript offers a limited update on research and related developments concerning the social support of visually impaired people subsequent to the preparation of the original report. It concludes with information about a current study by the author and colleagues which takes forward the main recommendations of the review.

Part I
THE STUDY IN CONTEXT

1 Background

The history of services for visually impaired people

Welfare services for visually impaired people have been available in this country in some form or other for many years. These services, and with them the terms used to identify the particular group of disabled people concerned, have developed in a somewhat piecemeal fashion. We shall first briefly consider this broad historical background.

Like most specialized areas of the welfare services in Britain, the roots of care for people with impaired vision lie in the history of the voluntary sector, reflecting the ways in which local communities and people with sight problems have themselves recognized and tried to meet apparent needs. Services provided by the statutory sector have essentially grown both alongside and out of those provided by voluntary organizations (Phelan, 1984; Abel, 1987, 1989).

The most prominent voluntary agency in this field is the Royal National Institute for the Blind (RNIB), which was founded in 1868 by Dr Rhodes Armitage, a surgeon who himself became blind. Together with other blind people he selected Braille as the most useful form of embossed literature and 'The British and Foreign Society for Improving Embossed Literature for the Blind', as what is now the RNIB was then called, became a leading publisher. Since that time, the RNIB has become involved in a very wide range of care and services for its client group and has undertaken a variety of research projects on their behalf (RNIB, 1987).

There are many other voluntary bodies in Britain concerned with visual impairment. Some have been established longer than the RNIB and most are locally based organizations set up to provide help in a specific locality or region. The history of changing attitudes to social care can to a significant extent be traced through the titles of these organizations, very many of which still include the now somewhat outmoded and 'uncomfortable' suffix '... for the Blind'. They are variously called 'Leagues', 'Societies', 'Welfare Societies' and 'Voluntary Societies', sometimes 'Institutes', 'Institutions' or 'Royal Institutions'. Voluntary organizations serving whole counties commonly call themselves 'Associations', perhaps indicating that they developed later than more local bodies and through the coming together of these smaller groups. Voluntary agencies in this field also include regionally based organizations and organizations which serve the interests of particular sub-groups, such as the Partially Sighted Society (PSS) and the National Deaf-Blind League (NDBL).

The growth in the size of the partially sighted population, and the trend away from direct service provision on the part of the statutory sector, are two important themes reflected in the reports and research examined in this review and in our discussion of future research needs.

An interesting, if anecdotal, insight into the interplay of influences on the naming of organizations is provided by the decision of Hampshire Association for the Care of the Blind to preface its title with 'Sight Concern Hampshire' (following the example of Age Concern). This is partly to indicate that people with low vision as well as blind people are welcome to contact the Association. It also seeks to suggest that the interests represented by the Association and its members, who can be visually impaired or normally sighted, go beyond the direct provision of 'care for' to a wider platform of the 'concerns of' people with sight loss. The retention of the earlier title, including '... for the Blind', no doubt reflects a necessary sensitivity to the perceptions of those who represent major and traditional sources of charitable income.

Accounts of the history of provision for visually impaired people (Abel, 1987, 1989; Phelan, 1984) indicate both persistent uncertainty and fluctuation over time as to how far and in what ways they have been and should be regarded as a special group amongst disabled people.

A series of Acts of Parliament has provided the changing framework for the provision of services by both the voluntary and statutory sectors. The most significant Acts are:

The Blind Persons Act 1920

The National Assistance Act 1948

The Social Services Act 1970

The Chronically Sick and Disabled Persons Act 1970

The Local Government Act 1972

The Disabled Persons (Service, Consultation and Representation) Act 1986

The Children Act 1989

The National Health Service and Community Care Act 1990.

A number of recent reports produced within or commissioned by the Department of Health have identified key factors bearing on future planning and service development:

OPCS Surveys of Disability in Great Britain (six reports) (1988 and 1989)

A Wider Vision: The Management and Organisation of Services for People who are Blind or Visually Handicapped (DHSS (SSI), 1988b)[1]

Sign Posts: Leading to Better Social Services for Deaf-Blind People (DoH (SSI), 1989)[2]

Co-ordinating Services for Visually Handicapped People: Report to the Minister for the Disabled (DoH, 1989b)

Caring for People: Community Care in the Next Decade and Beyond (DoH, 1989a).

Along with the most recent legislation among that listed above, in particular the NHS and Community Care Act 1990, these reports continue to represent a key part of the context for service development - and associated research - concerning the social support of visually impaired people over the coming years. Each is referred to at various points in this book, although it did not seem appropriate to include any of them as research projects in our Directory. As with other articles or books referred to in the text but not listed in the Directory, these reports (but not the Acts of Parliament) are referenced using the Harvard system, with full bibliographic details given in the collected References at the end of the book.

Most of the individual projects listed in the Directory are not included in the References. If referred to in the text they are referenced by means of the index number allocated to them, e.g. [3(o)5] (see Chapter 2 for a full explanation of this numbering system). A small number of the projects listed in the Directory, such as some of the substantial studies produced, commissioned and/or published in recent years by the RNIB, are sufficiently well known and influential under their published titles to be quoted in general discussion in the text. These are included in the References and where appropriate both a Harvard reference and an index number are given in the text: e.g. (Shore, 1985) [1A(c)3].

The Social Services Inspectorate (at the time DHSS, now DoH) report A Wider Vision (SSI, 1988b) gives a useful overview of the evolving role of the British State in the provision of services to visually impaired people. This is drawn upon in the following paragraphs.

In 1920, the Blind Persons Act defined blindness in the following terms:

> [A] person should be so blind as to be unable to perform any work for which eyesight is essential.

At this stage services were only directed towards the needs of those legally certified as blind.

The Act also required counties and county boroughs:

> to make arrangements to the satisfaction of the Minister of Health for promoting the welfare of the blind ordinarily resident in their area ...

'Welfare' in this context included workshops, homes and hostels, and the Act permitted local authorities to appoint local voluntary agencies for the blind to carry out these duties on their behalf.

The National Assistance Act of 1948 terminated the existing Poor Law and also repealed and replaced the 1920 Blind Persons Act. Under Section 29 of the Act, local authorities were required to make arrangements for the welfare of people substantially or permanently handicapped (the linguistic conventions of the Act are preserved here) by illness, injury or congenital deformity. Partially sighted as well as blind people were included, with the former thereby brought under the broader umbrella of local authority welfare services. *A Wider Vision* (SSI, 1988b, p. 47) lists the specific services which local authorities had to ensure were provided for visually impaired people in their areas. There was a strong emphasis on the employment of qualified 'home teachers of the blind', the provision of employment opportunities at home or in sheltered workshops, and the teaching of Moon and Braille. The 1948 Act (Section 30) allowed local authorities, in doing this, to continue to appoint voluntary organizations as their agents. Detailed practices in this respect have varied widely across the country.

Section 1(1) of the 1970 Chronically Sick and Disabled Persons Act requires local authorities:

> to inform themselves of the number of persons to whom Section 29 of the National Assistance Act 1948 applies.

DHSS Local Authority Circular 13/74 clarified what was mandatory and what permissive in relation to the 1948 and 1970 Acts. Maintaining registers of handicapped people was amongst the mandatory requirements, and many of those local authorities which had earlier passed responsibility for the registration and follow-up of blind or partially sighted people to local voluntary organizations now took over these duties themselves. However, much of the 1970 Act is permissive, and this legislation has consequently had less influence on the development of services for disabled people than many interested parties had hoped.

The Local Government Act 1972 repealed the requirement for individual schemes for separate client groups of handicapped people, scrutinized and approved by the Minister of Health, replacing this with arrangements by which local authorities were to undertake general duties, mandatory and permissive. This change has been seen as having a negative impact on provision for blind people, who had previously enjoyed some priority through the specific references to them contained in legislation.

Under the Disabled Persons (Service, Consultation and Representation) Act 1986, local authorities are required to assess the needs of individuals who are disabled in the terms of the National Assistance Act 1948, including visually impaired people, for the services listed in Section 2 of the Chronically Sick and Disabled Persons Act 1970 as necessary to meet the requirements of the 1948 Act. Section 47(2) of the NHS and Community Care Act 1990 explicitly confirms this entitlement under the Disabled Persons Act 1986. The 1990 Act also applies across the 'priority groups' and therefore includes disabled people in general and visually impaired people in particular.

The foregoing brief historical sketch of the development of what might best be termed non-medical services for people with impaired vision, including the legislative framework of such provision, has introduced a number of important themes.

For those whose sight problems are adventitious, rather than congenital or otherwise manifest at birth, referral to and assessment by social services departments for direct help with mobility and other aspects of daily living is of crucial importance. Such referral and assistance is associated, but not synonymous, with registration (see next section).

Employment rehabilitation is also a key area, at least for visually impaired people of working age. Education in the formal and/or narrower sense is perhaps - although not exclusively - more relevant to people whose sight is impaired from birth. However, in the more general sense of communication and 'life skills' there is a relevance to the wider group. All this notwithstanding, and for reasons argued in Chapter 2, our review did not seek to give detailed attention to research around education/communication or concerning employment. We addressed ourselves more focally to social care/support in a narrower sense, with a view to the interface with health services. This seemed most appropriate to the policy themes behind our study.

Changing views of the nature and extent of 'need'

It can be said that the needs and interests of disabled people, including those with a visual impairment, have begun to achieve a somewhat higher profile than they had in the recent past, both through legislation such as the 1986 Disabled Persons Act and in the actual provision of services. One significant reason for this lies is the acknowledgement of continuing demographic change, with a substantial increase in the numbers and proportion within the population who are over retirement age, particularly over the age of eighty, and a corresponding decrease in the proportion of the population who are of working age (Central Statistical Office (CSO), *Social Trends* 1990, p. 24, Table 1.2).

This demographic change has a particular and additional significance for the planning of services and support for visually impaired people, since provision in this field largely evolved around a model of a mentally and physically fit, but totally blind person, as a legacy from the development of services to meet the needs of war-blinded servicemen in addition to those for people born without sight. Now, however, a very high proportion of people with sight loss, as of those with other impairments, are over the age of retirement, are partially sighted rather than blind, and are as vulnerable as their normally sighted peer group to other disabilities or health problems associated with ageing (Cullinan, 1977; Cullinan and Silver, 1986; Neslen, 1989).

As already indicated, we did not include the recent *Surveys of Disability in Great Britain* (1988 and 1989), commissioned from OPCS by the Department of Health, in our listing of research relevant to social support for people with sight problems. This was because the frame of reference of the OPCS studies was very much wider than our own. However, relevant parts of the OPCS data formed an important aspect of the context of our review.

As discussed in the Preface to this book, an important theoretical and political critique of the conceptual framework employed by OPCS has been offered by the disability movement (Oliver, 1987, 1990; Abberley, 1991, 1992). This presses upon us a need to interpret the data produced by OPCS and similar subsequent work such as the RNIB Surveys (Bruce et al., 1991; Walker et al., 1992 (see Postscript)) within a wider perspective. However, the demographic picture provided by these studies remains an important backdrop for future discussion of both policy and service development, nationally and locally. Their main merit lies in pointing to a substantially higher incidence of visual impairment than was hitherto officially recognized.

The primary aim of the OPCS Surveys was:

> to provide estimates of the number of people ... with different levels of severity of disability. (*Report 1*, p. 6)

The authors conceived 'severity' in terms of a continuum, rather than in absolute terms, i.e. 'disabled' or 'not disabled'. They also sought explicitly to include all types of disability, rather than simply those with a physical origin, as had often been the case in earlier surveys.

In relation to the WHO definitions of impairment, disability and handicap (WHO, 1981; Wood 1980) (see Preface), the OPCS estimated that in 1991 there would be 1,668,000 adults and 22,000 children in the population of Great Britain with seeing disabilities (*OPCS Surveys, Report*

10

1, p. 25, Table 3.11, and *Report 3*, p. 24, Table 3.9 respectively). *A Wider Vision* (SSI, 1988b, pp. 5-6) quotes the *Initial Demographic Study* (Shankland Cox Partnerships, 1985a) and the *Second Demographic Study* (Shankland Cox Partnerships, 1985b), commissioned by the RNIB, as respectively estimating approximately 271,200 adults and 5,120 children likely to be registered as blind or partially sighted by 1991. Taken together, these data suggest that the presence of visual impairment in the general population is far higher than has been generally assumed, and that information based on registration is inadequate as a basis for resource and service planning. (See Postscript for the estimates offered by the later RNIB Surveys (Bruce et al., 1991; Walker et al., 1992).)

Much of the debate in response to the OPCS Surveys has focused on categories and degrees of handicap. I do not mean here the important critiques provided by the disability movement (see Preface), but rather the respective concerns of 'orthodox' researchers and politicians of various complexions to emphasize or limit the scale of 'the problem'. In general terms this need not detain us here, although several specific points are of some importance to our concerns.

One important feature of the overall profile of the sub-population of disabled people made up of those with a visual impairment reflects the fact that the majority of such people are elderly (*OPCS Surveys, Report 1*, p. 25, Table 3.13):

> Older people are more likely to have disabilities which put them in the higher severity categories. This is because many of the causes of disability are age-related, and because older people are more likely than younger ones to have more than one type of disability. (*OPCS Surveys, Report 4*, p. 3)

In addition, elderly people may not acknowledge having a visual impairment, because the deterioration of their sight has been slow (Calnan, 1981). They may regard it as a lesser difficulty than other health problems from which they suffer. They may also be unaware that help or advice is available, or they and/or their carers may be unwilling to seek it. This is one of several reasons why the number of people with significant degrees of visual loss is likely to be considerably higher than current registration data indicate.

A number of features of the registration process itself limit the identification of the visually impaired population, both individually and in aggregate; in particular the linkage between certification, registration, assessment for and receipt of appropriate social care services.

Eligibility for registration as either blind or partially sighted is certified (on Form BD8 (revised 1990)) by an ophthalmologist (usually a hospital consultant) on the basis of a clinical examination. Registration is effected by the social services department. The distinction between certification and registration is an important one, about which even the professionals

11

involved often fail to be clear.[3]

In most cases completion of the BD8 can be seen as effectively the beginning of a process which may lead to registration - although general practitioners will have referred the person to the specialist in the majority of cases, whilst opticians, and people working in social services departments or voluntary organizations, as well as individuals with sight problems, or their relatives, may well have taken the initial action, for example referral or self-referral to the GP.

The (1990) BD8 has two stand-alone sections. The first, comprising Parts 1-4, records certain information about the nature and degree of the person's visual impairment, as diagnosed by the ophthalmologist. There is a place for the visually impaired person's consent to be recorded, and if such consent is given the person's GP and the social services department in whose area the person lives receive copies, with the person her/himself and the ophthalmologist retaining the other two copies. The amount of clinical information recorded on the revised (1990) version of the BD8 is less than that on its (1968) predecessor. This was the result of lengthy discussion between the medical and other professions about what was useful to different agencies and the ethics of communicating information between them (DoH, 1989b). The second section, Part 5, does not include the individual's name and a copy is sent for statistical purposes to OPCS. The existence of this process of anonymous numerical recording, quite distinct from any contact with social services, but also using part of the BD8 completed by the ophthalmologist, may in part account for the confusion mentioned above between what constitutes certification and what registration. In so far as it is complete, OPCS data strictly provides an annual aggregate picture of the extent of certified eligibility for registration.

There is evidence that people with sight problems are not necessarily clear about the nature and cause of their difficulties, or what help they might be able to obtain. This is due in part to the quality of the information made available to them by ophthalmologists and para-medical services in the context of certification.

In this respect, the OPCS Surveys found that:

> Not surprisingly 86 per cent of seeing disabilities were said to be caused by eye complaints, but here the limits of the respondents' knowledge were apparent. Only a minority were able to give a specific eye complaint - 20 per cent mentioned cataracts for example - while 62 per cent could give no further details. (*Report 4*, p. 11)

and that:

> The proportion of children with seeing disabilities was relatively small, 6 per cent, but not surprisingly over half (53 per cent) of

such disabilities were caused by eye complaints. The limit of parents' knowledge was apparent here as only a few were able to give a specific eye complaint - 8 per cent mentioned cataracts for example - while 41 per cent could give no further details of the cause of their child's sight problems. (*Report 6*, p. 12)

There is also evidence of difficulties around the registration process. For example, time lags can exist between an ophthalmologist's certification of eligibility and receipt of the BD8 by the local authority, delays can occur in the social services department making initial contact with the person concerned, effecting registration (if so-desired), carrying out an assessment, and actually providing one or more types of help.

The visits reported in *A Wider Vision* (SSI, 1988b) led the Inspectors to the view that:

[Since] all authorities provided written instructions on how to deal with ... [BD8s] ... in the absence of anything else, the *form* had actually become the policy statement. (p. 13) [emphasis in original]

The comment continues:

The referral procedure on the form BD8 generally elicited a narrow limited response from agencies towards people designated as blind or partially sighted. (ibid.)

A further limitation on the adequacy of aggregate registration data as a proxy for overall need is, as we have seen, that people certified as eligible by an ophthalmologist can choose not to be registered. A belief that registration (especially as partially sighted) conveys very little in terms of substantive benefit - and a sense of stigmatization associated with the idea of being on a register - have usually been seen as responsible for this. The other side of this coin - and a further factor in the elusive relationship between registration data and aggregate need - is the fact that non-registration does not preclude access to certain forms of help.

Thus there is accumulated evidence of various sorts questioning the accuracy of the information held by the relevant statutory and voluntary agencies on the aggregate and individual needs of people in their areas with various forms and degrees of visual impairment. This is in large part a reflection of features of the registration process, on which such information depends heavily.

The certification/registration process is also itself (and for other reasons such as those indicated in the above discussion) a long-standing cause of concern. The inspections reported in *A Wider Vision* (SSI, 1988b) have already been referred to. Shaw (1985) had examined some of these matters earlier, in a particular local setting, concentrating on the social services department. There was extensive discussion of the registration process in

Co-ordinating Services for Visually Handicapped People (DoH, 1989b). We anticipated receiving further material relevant to these important themes in the course of our review, in particular from social services departments and voluntary organizations. In fact relatively little emerged from these sources.

In addition to the influence on policy of a degree of acknowledgement of the demographic factors referred to in the foregoing discussion, there has been a considerable 'philosophical' shift in recent years, not least within agencies directly providing services. The general perspective has moved from one based on providing care for disabled people, who were thus by implication passive recipients, to one of seeing them as having a legitimate 'voice'. Direct service users and their carers are now commonly acknowledged as having a right to choice and a right to take part in shaping services in partnership with professionals. These developments have been significantly influenced by the articulation of their own expectations by disabled people themselves.

The values often referred to in this context as 'consumerism', or more recently 'empowerment', are now widely shared. In recent years these notions have been intertwined in policy debates and in the actual development of welfare provision with questions around the accountability of public services and, more narrowly, with continuing concern on the part of central and, partly by extension, local government to control public expenditure. A further strand, variously presented as intimately connected with 'cost-effectiveness' and/or as an important guarantor of choice, has been the pressure towards a 'mixed economy of care', with statutory agencies no longer the sole or main direct providers of services. The variety of meanings of 'empowerment', in particular the differences between interpretations crucially linked to citizenship and rights and others centring around choice in 'free' markets, bear on these matters.

This mixture of ideas has been evident for some years in official reports and legislation, including in relation to disability in general and visual impairment in particular. The White Paper *Caring for People* (DoH, 1989a), and the subsequent NHS and Community Care Act 1990, embodied many of these themes with regard to the overall field of social care. Crystallizing as we prepared the original report on our review, this specific 'new agenda' - i.e. that of implementing 'community care' - provided the most appropriate context for considering future research priorities in relation to the social support needs of people with impaired vision (see Chapter 7).

Notes

1   Reports produced by the Social Services Inspectorate (SSI), now part of the Department of Health (DoH) and initially part of the then Department of Health and Social Security (DHSS), are listed in Refer-

ences under the parent Department applicable at the date of a particular publication, and in a form equivalent to the following: DHSS (SSI), 1988b. In the text, however, following the occurrence to which this note relates, the convention (SSI, 1988b) or similar will be employed. (The full form has been used in all instances in the Preface.)

2 See note 1.
3 For recent confirmation of this at first somewhat surprising phenomenon, see Rumney (1992) and Thomas (1991). Current research in which the present author is involved (see Postscript) has offered further evidence. See also the recent review of BD8 procedures commissioned by the Department of Health from Insight Management Consulting (1994).

2 Aims and methods

Aims of the review

The work which the Department of Health commissioned from CEDR was described formally as a review of 'recent and current research concerning blind and partially sighted subjects'. The research brief acknowledged the 'many common issues in the rehabilitation field which relate to all types of disability', but required only work specifically including people with a visual impairment. This reflected the Department's wish to 'realign and update' its research programme in the area of social support and services for visually impaired people, in response to accumulating evidence concerning the demographic profile of the population with significant sight problems. Chapter 1 has offered more detailed background information on this. The feeling was that most of the social research recently funded by the Department in this area was, although valuable, somewhat narrowly focused; the future programme should better reflect the broad spectrum of needs of the client group(s) concerned, and give greater attention to associated questions about the most appropriate forms of provision and about service organization, delivery and funding.

The formal aims of the review, developed in the light of this brief, set out in the research proposal, and accepted by the Department, were:

1. To list all relevant studies ongoing or completed in the previous three years, including evaluated development initiatives. In each case giving title, researcher(s)/organizational base, the timescale and size (in 'researcher weeks') of the study, its cost and funding body, an

abstract of the purpose and methods of the study, its current status, a summary of findings (where complete), and the date, cost and availability of any report(s) and/or other associated publications or dissemination activities.

2. To structure this information in terms of more detailed subject areas, nature and source(s) of funding, scale and coverage.

3. To summarize recent findings and ongoing work by means of an analytic essay, and to identify areas needing further attention, as a basis for consideration of the content and priorities of a revised national programme of research concerning social care and services for blind and partially sighted people, to be supported by the Department of Health and other appropriate bodies.

Methodology and conduct of the review

Two main sources were used to identify potentially relevant research. Firstly, a postal *pro forma* was sent to all local authority social services departments in England, the agreement of the Association of Directors of Social Services (ADSS) having been sought and obtained through their Research Committee. This consciously acknowledged the key role of social services departments in relation to service provision and their demonstrated capacity to undertake research of an operational nature, sometimes jointly and/or in collaboration with academic or other bodies. An identical enquiry was sent to a selection of voluntary organizations drawn from the latest available RNIB directory (RNIB, 1987a). Broadly speaking, national bodies were included, along with local organizations with a county or large town/city frame of reference. After a variety of initial consultations we decided against equivalent general approaches in the health services field. The second source of possible work for inclusion consisted of a variety of research indexes, abstracts and bibliographic databases. These were used to identify potentially relevant academic research and studies based in independent research institutes. Direct contact was then made with the researchers concerned, usually by telephone, with one or more *pro formas* subsequently despatched, where appropriate, to obtain information comparable to that requested from social services departments and voluntary agencies.

Not all of the research institutes whom we thought might be working in the field of visual impairment turned out to have relevant recent or current work to report. In these cases, no *pro formas* were despatched following initial contact.

Not all of the specific projects identified as potentially relevant proved to be so. For example, library searches threw up rather more material which turned out not really to be based on research than they did studies

17

of which we were otherwise unaware.

Similarly, some returns from social services departments or voluntary organizations were discounted as offering information on activities which could not be said to constitute research, even on a liberal interpretation. Such material was not included in the listing of projects, but proved useful as background to the discussion of the collection of work which was included.

A number of funding bodies were approached for listings of projects supported, partly as a cross-reference or 'double-check' as regards material located via other sources. Similarly, the Research Handbooks or equivalent of the relevant central government departments were examined. In neither case was significant new information identified. In fact, requests to funding bodies, including some very major ones, produced a very poor response, which was taken to indicate that most were not funding work in this field.

Independently of these general approaches, four bodies known to be prominently involved in our field of concern were contacted direct at an early stage of the exercise. These were: the Blind Mobility Research Unit (BMRU), based in the Department of Psychology at the University of Nottingham; the Research Centre for the Education of the Visually Handicapped (RCEVH), located at the School of Education, University of Birmingham; the London Headquarters of the Royal National Institute for the Blind (RNIB); and the National Foundation for Educational Research NFER) based at Slough. The first and last named were the main recent beneficiaries of research monies from the Department of Health for work in the relevant area. Half-day visits were made at a later stage to the first three of these bodies; all four supplied detailed material, including a number of completed *pro formas*.

A total of 221 *pro formas* were despatched, with an overall response rate of seventy-four per cent after one follow-up letter. Fifty-seven (twenty-six per cent) of the specific enquiries received no reply or (in three instances) were returned as incorrectly addressed. 'Nil returns' were requested and 133 (sixty per cent) were received. This high level of 'nil returns' represents a finding in itself, indicating the limited amount of research work being carried out in this field by social services departments and specialist voluntary organizations.

Thirty-one respondent bodies (fourteen per cent) reported relevant completed or ongoing studies, some of them enclosing reports and/or other information about their work. A number of multiple responses were received, i.e. information about several studies was supplied. As anticipated, this was particularly the case in respect of the two major specialist research centres (BMRU and RCEVH) and the RNIB. Several other organizations submitted two, three or four *pro formas*. Some responses indicated joint projects, although in most of these cases, even where the reported partner organization had also been approached in our survey, we received no duplicate or parallel response. In the very small number of instances where two notifications of the same project were received, single entries were prepared, with the joint nature of the studies concerned indicated. The final listing of projects in the form of a Directory (see Appendix) contains sixty-nine individual entries.

As already outlined, following preliminary discussion, the majority of academic and independent research bodies approached either had nothing relevant for inclusion and so were not sent *pro formas*, or had several relevant studies to report and completed one or more individual returns. The remaining requests, replies, positive responses and 'nil returns' were each relatively evenly split between the other broad groupings: social services departments and voluntary bodies.

The study formally commenced on 1 September 1989, with a report date seven months later: i.e. 31 March 1990. Delays in obtaining ADSS support and ensuring that the survey instruments to be used were acceptable to the Department of Health meant that *pro formas* could not be despatched until shortly before Christmas 1989. Two subsequent periods of illness on the part of the contract researcher, and the emerging scale of the task in relation to what had seemed likely at the outset, led to subsequent revisions to the timescale - although not to the budget - for the project. There were two changes of Research Liaison Officer (i.e. our main point of contact within the Department of Health) during the course of the work. A preliminary report was submitted in July 1990, with the full final report accepted in July 1991.

Problems of definition

A key difficulty, evident from the outset, was how to draw appropriate boundaries concerning the main subject matter of the review. Given the particular field concerned, the overall aims of the study, the current general policy context and debate as regards social and health care, and recent increased attention to the special needs of people with dual sensory impairment and people with severe learning difficulties as well as visual or dual sensory loss, these definitional problems could not be resolved entirely satisfactorily at the outset - or for that matter at the conclusion - of the study. They had been addressed in the agreed research proposal and were further refined in the context of the letter to respondents requesting information and introducing our *pro forma*. They arose again in the context of how best to structure and summarize the material collected. They reflect substantive concerns in the field and therefore have a direct bearing on future research priorities.

The framework set for respondents and for ourselves had the following main elements:

- the main focus was to be projects completed/published from 1986 to the date of contact, plus ongoing work

- development initiatives were only to be included where they had been/were being systematically evaluated and reported upon

- internal or otherwise limited circulation reports would potentially be acceptable, as well more widely distributed and/or more formal/refereed publications

- relevant work was that concerning blind and/or partially sighted people, but not people with sight problems correctable by 'ordinary spectacles'

- work concerning disabled people in general, e.g. overall surveys of need, was to be included only if visually impaired groups were specifically identified within it

- the focus on social care/services was to be taken to imply the exclusion of research on clinical/medical treatment, although in including/excluding studies the important potential overlap in terms of onward referral for rehabilitation and continuing support was to be acknowledged

- work not relevant to the primary concerns of the Department of Health, but rather to those of Departments such as Social Security, Employment, Education or Transport, was not to be a major focus, although possible overlaps would be taken into account in deciding whether to include/exclude a study.

In advising potential respondents, we recommended as a general rule that if in any doubt information should be supplied, thus seeking to reserve the ultimate decision on inclusion or exclusion to ourselves. A number of telephone calls were received and answered on points of definition.

The approach taken had as a consequence the strong possibility that at the boundaries some respondents included work of a kind which others excluded. Whilst we were able to exclude work reported which we deemed not to be relevant to our concerns, we clearly could not decide to include studies of which we had not been informed. Thus we cannot be sure that complete coverage was obtained, especially in certain areas. A particular example concerns work relevant to the special needs of people with dual sensory or multiple impairments. In our original proposal we signalled our intention to exclude work relating to 'severely multi-handicapped groups' (sic) such as people born deaf-blind and/or with what would now be termed severe learning difficulties as well as a visual impairment or dual sensory loss, as we had been advised to do by our Research Liaison Officer in preliminary discussion. However, we could find no satisfactory and straightforward way of defining boundaries on this point for the purposes of a postal survey, so we left the matter implicitly open. Similar boundary issues arose concerning studies in the areas of employment, education and transport. We did not survey agencies with major responsibilities in these fields, but we did examine the research handbooks or equivalent of the appropriate central government departments. Specific questions about inclusion/exclusion in fact arose mainly in respect of work by some of the major organizations with whom we had established direct contact, rather than with the bulk of postal respondents. These were resolved in discussion.

Some further points are worthy of note here. Welsh social services departments and voluntary bodies were excluded from our postal survey. This was a purely pragmatic decision, taken jointly by the researchers and the Research Liaison Officer concerned. On reflection, it would probably have been appropriate and useful to have included Welsh agencies. Secondly, as part of seeking to clarify the parameters of our enquiries for potential respondents, we took our initial bearings from the commissioning brief's reference to 'blind and partially sighted people', with the attendant consequence of possible over-identification with certification and registration criteria in some respondents' minds. It might have been preferable to have used the terms 'impairment' and 'disability' making the distinctions discussed here in the Preface, or, given the conventions of the time, to have drawn directly on the WHO nomenclature (i.e. including 'handicap' as a third term) (WHO, 1981; Wood, 1980) (see Preface and Chapter 1).

A final topic, demanding further brief mention at this point, concerns health service/medical research material. We were particularly keen to identify any studies which examined issues at the health/social care interface, since we saw this as central to the context of the review and to future policy and practice as well as to research. Nevertheless, for reasons already given, we decided to approach this mainly from 'non-health' 'directions', although in the course of our investigations we examined the Medical Research Council's Handbook for each of several years and attempted to contact a number of bodies known to fund medical and health services research. In the context of a somewhat belated direct discussion with representatives of the relevant 'customer' sections within the Department of Health (i.e. from the appropriate sections of Health Care Administration and of the SSI), in May 1990, we were invited to undertake further searches in the medical research literature and to contact a small number of named persons in the medical world. Both of these suggestions were taken up, but the additional work failed to lead to the identification of additional studies appropriate to include in our review and from, as it were, 'the health side of the health/social care interface'.

Whilst these recurrent methodological difficulties remain an important part of the context for interpreting the material which follows, we are confident that we achieved a satisfactory coverage of the relevant studies in our major field of concern. The definitional problems themselves are not without their more substantive importance, since they reflect the way in which disability issues and services straddle a number of fields, especially health/medicine and social care, with the constant danger that research and provision mirror each other in their relative failure to make or facilitate the appropriate connections.

Rationale and framework for listing studies

To provide the structured listing of recent and current research required by our brief, the studies reported to us and deemed eligible for inclusion were grouped in a manner which seemed most readily to organize the material concerned; i.e. the categories used 'emerged from the data'. The main sections of the Directory (see Appendix) thus reflect 'reality' in terms of research activity at the time of the review as evidenced by the overall response to our enquiries.

The first level - the main or primary element - of structuring (and indexing - see below) was that the studies to be included were grouped in terms of their subject matter according to eight broad themes. The first group of studies was further sub-divided. The themes/groups developed in this way were as follows:

1 Service organization and strategy, client need, service initiatives

    A   Reviews of service organization and strategy

    B   Client based surveys of need

    C   Evaluations of service initiatives

2 Low vision/partial sight

3 Mobility

4 Training of specialist staff, and assessment and training of visually impaired people

5 Dual sensory impairment[1]

6 Multiple impairment including sight loss[2]

7 Education

8 Employment

The themes represented by these groupings overlap to some degree, whilst the groupings themselves are not all of the same conceptual order or type. Thirdly, with reference to the definitional and boundary issues already discussed, the material contained in Sections 5-8 inclusive must be considered likely to be incomplete to varying degrees. This is particularly so as regards Sections 7 and 8, which strictly lay outside our agreed remit. Within each of these main sections, entries were grouped according to whether the work concerned had been 'completed' or was 'ongoing' when information was supplied. In some cases further information had become available by the time the report on the review was being prepared, indicating whether or not a study reported earlier as likely to be completed within the next few months had in fact come to fruition. If so, the relevant entry reflected this. However, systematic re-contacting of all respondents, to ensure that the Directory as a whole was fully up-to-date when the final report was submitted was not possible.[3]

Each project identified for inclusion was given a unique reference number. The first digit of this is the number, 1 to 8, of the section under which a full entry is included in the Directory. In the case of Section 1, the first 'number' is to be understood as 1A, 1B or 1C. The second, bracketed, component of a project's reference number reflects whether the study was completed (c) or ongoing (o) in the terms indicated in the previous paragraph. Within this second level of structure, individual projects are listed and numbered in alphabetical order of their titles. The Directory of projects runs in order from 1A(c)1 to 8(o)2.

In order to present individual entries in the most useful form for people referring to the Directory, the information collected via the *pro formas* was re-ordered. Substantial editorial work was also necessary to standardize the entries as far as possible.

Each full project entry gives the name and address of the organization and - where reported to us - the researcher(s) concerned, with a contact telephone number. There is then an abstract concerning the subject matter, aims and methods of the project, and an indication of its coverage in terms of subjects or sample population and geographical scope. Where appropriate and possible there is a summary of findings and an indication of the availability of report(s), plus full bibliographical references to any additional publications. Where sufficient information was supplied, there is also an indication of the project's scale in terms of cost, total researcher weeks devoted to the study and overall lapsed time, and of the relevant funding body/ies.

A summary listing of projects, mirroring the overall structuring just outlined, and giving a page reference to the full entry in each case, precedes the sixty-nine individual entries in the Appendix, in effect as the latter's Contents. Some individual studies were felt to be potentially relevant under more than one main section heading. In these cases, one full entry only appears, in what is judged to be the most appropriate section. The summary listing/Contents indicates for each section which additional entries, located in other sections, are also particularly relevant to the focus of the section concerned.

Two additional indexes are provided, following the full entries. The first of these groups the organizations responsible for the studies according to the 'sector' to which they belong: essentially local authority, voluntary organization, or academic/independent research institute. Responsible organizations are listed alphabetically within these groupings and, where more than one study was notified by a particular organization, project titles are listed alphabetically under the organization concerned. The second index is an overall list, in alphabetical order by title, of all the projects included. In each of these additional indexes, relevant project numbers are given, along with a page reference locating the respective full entries.

Notes

1   This section was originally entitled 'deaf-blind people'. Although the term deaf-blind (now commonly deafblind) is still in use, for example in the titles of organizations such as the National Deaf-Blind League and the National Deaf-Blind and Rubella Association (SENSE), the heading for this group of projects was revised during preparation of this book, to reflect more widely used contemporary terms.
2   Originally entitled 'multi-handicapped and mentally handicapped people'. Revised in preparing this book for similar reasons to those indicated in note 1.
3   Neither has further systematic updating of the Directory been under-taken in preparing this book (see Preface, Postscript and Appendix). However, the addresses and telephone numbers shown in individual entries have recently (November 1994) been checked as far as possible and amended as necessary.

Part II
THE RESEARCH REVIEWED

Introduction

The research material identified and collated in the context of our review is presented in the four chapters making up Part II of this book (see below), which summarizes relevant recent research and places it in an historical context. This discussion reflects the structure of the Directory (see Appendix), considering each of the latter's sections in turn. The rationale for this structure was outlined in Chapter 2. The detailed practical application of the categories involved is not without its difficulties, as the following paragraphs briefly indicate.

Most of the studies included in the Directory fall into one of two groups. Either they represent the contributions of one or other of a small number of specialist academic or independent research centres, or they emanate from social services departments or local (or small national) voluntary sector organizations. The first body of work tends not to be overtly concerned with policy and practice, at least not in an immediate sense. Studies in the second group, conversely, are mostly oriented towards service planning or delivery, and are also (and quite appropriately) mainly local in coverage and frame of reference. In addition, this latter work tends in one way or another either to be extremely general or highly specific in its subject matter, and in neither case very detailed or rigorous in addressing it, for example commonly taking existing definitions and ways of meeting 'need' for granted. Moreover, research in these local authority or voluntary sector settings is likely to be of a somewhat *ad hoc* nature, rather than being part of a programme sustained over time.

There are some important exceptions to these rather sweeping general-

27

izations; most notably, the RNIB must immediately be associated with the specialist academic centres in terms of the scale, depth and differentiation of the subject matter of those of its research activities included here. The RNIB's studies are, however, strongly policy driven, although essentially by its own, rather than a fully national, policy agenda. To some extent the active and nationally relevant research programme reported by the Partially Sighted Society (PSS) also sets it somewhat apart from most other relatively small voluntary sector bodies. The Bristol Royal Society for the Blind (BRSB) has also produced evidence of its being another local voluntary organization with a strong commitment to research, in which context it, like the PSS, has worked closely with statutory agencies in its region.

These observations bear on certain difficulties concerning the extent to which some of the studies listed fit readily within the categories employed. To some extent, this variation in the 'fit' of particular studies into the overall schema correlates with the organizational base of the work concerned: local authority, voluntary agency, or academic/independent research institution. This is discussed specifically at appropriate points in the following chapters; its substantive dimensions have implications for some of the conclusions drawn from the review, and inform the recommendations contained in Part III, where it is addressed further.

In general terms it is some of the work of the main academic units which least readily fits into one or other of our groupings. This difficulty is a direct result of the specialist nature and focus of the few major and established British centres undertaking sustained social research on visual impairment issues, as against the very different levels and kinds of research attention given to the specific area of visual impairment by an 'all-purpose' research section (or similar) in an average local authority social services department, or the research resources likely to be available to most small local voluntary organizations.

The Blind Mobility Research Unit, based at the University of Nottingham, not only provided the largest single body of contributions to our listing and review; specific items of its work are also the most difficult to place in terms of the categories we have adopted. At the time of our review, the BMRU had a unique role.[1] At any one time its programme has included a number of precisely defined projects, reflecting several broader, but nevertheless specialized themes within the subject area. Inevitably, both the broad themes and the more specific elements of the Unit's work reflect a much greater degree of analytic separation than most research based in a local social services department or voluntary agency. Hence the difficulties in allocating specific BMRU projects to the categories selected to provide a useful classification across the whole body of work identified.

We gained the impression whilst conducting the study that a variety of interesting and relevant developmental work relevant to the social support of visually impaired people had been and was being undertaken, mainly under the auspices of social services departments and voluntary organizations. Such publications as emanate from such work are often not based on research or systematic and reported evaluation. In the present context, examples to which this applied were not included in our listing. However, this kind of activity, in so far as we were made aware of it, constitutes additional background to the discussion.

Chapter 3 examines the body of work grouped in Section 1 of the Directory under the broad heading 'service organization and strategy, client need, service initiatives', with its three sub-sections focusing respectively upon 'reviews of service organization and strategy, 'client based surveys of need', and 'evaluations of service initiatives'. Chapter 4 considers material listed in Sections 2, 3 and 4 of the Directory, i.e. those containing work specifically concerning the inter-related topics of 'low vision/partial sight', 'mobility', and 'training of specialist staff, and assessment and training of visually impaired people'. Chapter 5 discusses the studies listed in the four remaining sections of the Directory. For reasons given in Chapter 2 (see also Chapter 5 itself) the categorizations involved are of a different order and coverage is less likely to be complete than in Sections 1-4. The studies concerned are those notified relevant to the needs of people with dual sensory impairment, or people with multiple impairments including sight loss - for example people with severe learning difficulties in addition to visual or dual sensory impairment, or those which focus upon the education or employment of visually impaired people.

Some of the projects listed and discussed represent various forms of collaboration involving one or more statutory and/or voluntary agencies. Individually, these are outlined in discussing the particular group of studies within which each has been listed. Chapter 6 offers an additional, brief, and separate discussion of the varying forms of collaboration - particularly financial - which they reflect.

Notes

1   See Postscript for a brief indication of the BMRU's more recent situation.

3 Service organization and strategy, client need, service initiatives

In the main, the studies in Section 1 of the Directory as a whole had been or were being undertaken by local authorities or by voluntary organizations. Both national and local voluntary agencies are represented, whilst the local authority work is dominated by studies based in social services departments.

Generally, although not in all cases, the local authority studies relied heavily upon departmental registers and other records, and were directed towards reviewing procedures and/or developing strategies; their starting points tended to be existing services and records of current clients. Generally, although not in all cases, the studies coming from the voluntary sector, particularly those conducted by local organizations, tended to start more directly from the actual or potential client group, seeking to identify their needs, often in their own terms, and to approach organizational and managerial issues in that light. Some social services departments had interviewed service users, although usually only a very small sample. The interview based research which social services departments had carried out in this field had most commonly involved their own staff and/or colleagues in other statutory and voluntary agencies.

These rather broad generalizations may well reflect the different frames of reference typical of local authorities and voluntary organizations. In part at least the latter operate essentially as pressure groups, and seek improved services; for them *potential* service users represent a larger and perhaps therefore more persuasive reference point than *actual* users or registered visually impaired people. Local authorities tend to be reactive and to be wary of stimulating further demand, with in turn has implications for resources. Much of the work included in this section was quite appropriately of mainly very local focus and relevance, often reflecting issues or needs experienced as especially pressing by a particular agency at a particular time. However, the RNIB has a specifically national frame of reference, whilst the studies by or involving the Partially Sighted Society are among a number of other entries with a relevance beyond their immediate local settings and concerns.

There are some examples of joint work involving local and health authorities, one or other of these and the voluntary sector, or a health authority and a voluntary organization. Whilst several of these studies adopted what was essentially an organizational focus, particularly those involving the two main statutory authorities, it is significant that the collaborative studies listed include the very small number of projects identified which critically examined specific service initiatives. The identification and analysis of existing examples of good practice within their own services was not generally the main rationale of the local authority projects reported.

It is useful to divide the material included in Section 1 into three groups for more detailed discussion, dealing respectively with reviews of service organization and strategy, client based surveys of need, and evaluations of service initiatives. Adopting this approach will illustrate the generalizations made so far and make more evident the exceptions to them.

Reviews of service organization and strategy

Although this sub-section contains a significant majority of projects based in social services departments, the two major RNIB studies [1A(c)3] and [1A(c)8] are in many ways the most significant entries. By virtue of its publication date, *Local Authority Social Rehabilitation Services to Visually Handicapped People* [1A(c)3], widely known as 'the Shore Report' (Shore, 1985), strictly fell outside the parameters of our review. We included it, however, since its findings and recommendations remain pertinent and it has been a specific reference point for more recent work.

Based on a sample of nineteen local authority social services departments, and drawing upon interviews with staff and service users among a variety of information sources, Shore's research emphasized that the majority of the known population of visually impaired people was elderly, and that public information on available services and eligibility for them was inadequate. There was a lack of early intervention, a low level of provision of rehabilitation services, particularly for elderly people with sight problems, and a lack of stimulating and satisfying leisure and recreational facilities.

31

Shore's sample survey of clients revealed a high level of interest in rehabilitation, and a preference for rehabilitation services close to their homes rather than in residential centres. Local authorities felt that the most successful services were centrally organized ones in urban areas. Staff said that the demand for training in daily living skills was high but the demand for teaching communication skills and crafts was low. There were also differing views about the function and value of counselling in the rehabilitation process. Notwithstanding these gaps between service provision and felt need, the majority of the clients surveyed appeared satisfied with the services they received.

Shore noted the degree to which social services departments were dependent upon referrals from ophthalmologists via certification on Form BD8, and uncovered a wide variety of practices within and between local authorities in the management of the process of registration and in assessment for and delivery of services.

Shore indicated the low priority given to visually impaired people relative to other groups, as evidenced by poor staffing levels - five social services departments in the sample had no mobility officer and among the others the client/worker ratio varied between 208:1 and 1512:1 - and poor standards of staff supervision and managerial support. An ageist attitude in the provision of services was also detected:

> Whereas 90 per cent of all respondents aged between 20 and 49 had been offered rehabilitation, only 31 per cent of those aged 65+ claimed to have been given the same opportunity.

The Shore Report was also one of the first studies to draw the attention of social services departments to the lack of services available to meet the needs of blind or partially sighted people with additional/multiple impairments.

Although on a smaller scale than Shore's work, Thomas's study of *The Registration and Continuing Care of People with a Visual Impairment* [1A(c)4] also paid some attention to the national picture. His work was carried out with the aid of a Personal Social Services Fellowship, undertaken at the University of Bristol on secondment from his post as social work team manager at Bristol Eye Hospital. Thomas reviewed local resources and registration procedures, finding similar variations to those identified by Shore. He also critically examined the service provision models adopted by a number of other local authorities. His report, which was published by the Bristol Royal Society for the Blind in conjunction with the County of Avon Social Services Department, identified the advantages and disadvantages of having (teams of) specialist workers. It also drew attention to the need for services to take account of the differing needs of visually impaired people from ethnic minorities.

Whilst several of the listed reviews of service organization carried out by social services departments had taken recent Government and other national reports as their starting point, their focus, as already indicated, was almost invariably upon an immediate local context. An overview of the research listed in this sub-section suggests that the local authorities represented - and perhaps others - were at the time of our review at similar stages in beginning seriously to assess the needs of, and develop appropriate services for, visually impaired people. The main findings of the Shore Report appeared still to be applicable:

- the needs of visually impaired clients have been accorded a low priority in relation to those of other clients of social services departments

- social services departments experience difficulties in maintaining and managing their registers of blind and partially sighted people

- specialist staff are scarce and have not fitted easily into the variety and often succession of operational and management structures which have been developed over the last few decades, although little attention has been given to this problem

- visually impaired clients with additional disabilities do not fit easily into the service systems designed with reference to a single 'category' of client; also, any one local authority area is likely to have relatively small numbers in such special needs groups (see RNIB (Deaf-Blind Services Liaison Group), 1988 [5(c)1]; Best et al., 1987 [6(c)3]).

The studies reported seemed to indicate limited and variable collaboration between social services departments and other relevant agencies, with a relative lack of awareness on all sides of the 'social' dimension of the needs of visually impaired people. Local authority research typically seemed to have paid or to be paying insufficient attention to identifying examples of good practice, although these might well exist.

A specific issue was the sharing of information, such as that from registers of various kinds, between agencies, including statutory authorities in the same area. For example, the Hampshire *Survey of Needs* [1B(c)3] discovered indirectly that the local Education Department was aware of far more visually impaired children than were registered with either the Social Services Department or the Hampshire Association for the Care of the Blind, indicating the need for appropriate procedures for sharing information on children with sight loss. The 1981 Education Act, the 1986 Disabled Persons Act, and the 1989 Children Act all include the aim of improving the standards of services for disabled children; however, as with unregistered adults, it is difficult to identify and reach children and families who may have no reason to be, or who have not yet reached the stage of being, formally brought to the notice of the relevant education and/or social services authorities.

The foregoing rather general observations have necessarily not been very specific *vis à vis* particular studies. Although most substantive local authority returns were supported by copies of research reports, we were advised in several cases that the contents either could not be made public in an attributable way or that special permission would be necessary from the relevant committee or chief officer. It was clear in a number of cases that this reflected the fact that recommendations based on the research had not been accepted or implemented. It is of some concern that potentially valuable information on clients, their needs, and service developments in local authority social services departments, is not made more freely available. This is in addition to the point made earlier, and which is evident from the high proportion of 'nil returns' in response to our survey, that relatively few social services departments were carrying out systematic research relevant to visual impairment issues. Some 'nil returns' completed by research staff personally known to the author indicated a clear sense that, whilst little work relevant to our review had been done in their authority, there was a strong case for paying greater attention to the field it had focused upon.

Our review indicated two further ways in which both visually impaired people and the specialist staff working with them were perhaps being rendered 'invisible'. Four social services departments sent details of and reports on general surveys of physically disabled or elderly clients which contained no information specifically identifying people with sight problems. These returns were excluded from our Directory, since they did not meet the stated criteria for inclusion, but it seems probable, given the guidelines given to respondents, that other departments had done or were doing similar work but did not report it. *A Wider Vision* (SSI, 1988b) reported that local authorities commonly surveyed elderly populations without obtaining information on sight (and hearing and speech) problems. Secondly, staff specializing in work with visually impaired people were not separately identified in the nationally collated *Local Authority Social Services Statistics: Staff of Local Authority Social Services Departments*, the latest available version of which was (at the time of our review) for the year to 30 September 1985 (DHSS, 1987a). The low status accorded to some professionals working with visually impaired people by other professionals in the same field was one of the issues which the South Devon Review and Planning Group, with which the Partially Sighted Society was closely associated, hoped to overcome with its model of an inter-disciplinary team [1A(c)6].

Like other recent RNIB research projects, and the policy and planning papers which they have informed (e.g. RNIB, 1987b), the Shore Report (1985) [1A(c)3] was primarily concerned with the future development of the Institute's own services. Specifically, Shore addressed the 'role of the RNIB in the future of social rehabilitation', recommending the establishment of consultancy services to enable local authority staff to extend their knowledge of rehabilitation resources and services, and urging RNIB to further develop its own rehabilitation expertise, including its residential resources. Shore also suggested that co-ordination between RNIB and social services departments would be facilitated if the former developed on a regional basis.

Regional development and improved information dissemination were recurrent themes in recent RNIB publications, and some initiatives had been taken. A consultancy service had been established and was working with a number of local health and social services agencies, particularly in the North West of England. Oldham Health Authority, and the Social Services Departments of Lancashire County Council and both Oldham and Tameside Metropolitan Authorities, had each been involved. A report on *Visually Disabled Services in Tameside* had been completed [1A(c)7], but it could only be obtained with the permission of the Director of Social Services. Other similar exercises were under way when our survey took place.

Working Together: The Scope for Improving Working Links between RNIB and Local Societies for the Blind (Lomas and Vaughan, 1987) [1A(c)8] again evidenced the RNIB's concern to improve and develop its own services, and in this case in particular its relationships with other voluntary organizations. However, the general findings of the study appeared to be of interest to a wider audience, with implications for the development of joint work between local authorities, health authorities and voluntary organizations. This entry also represents the only work reported to us reviewing the policy and practice of voluntary organizations in this context. In fact, Lomas and Vaughan found that the societies surveyed had 'surprisingly little contact' with RNIB, beyond making use of aids and various professional services.

Lomas and Vaughan found no standard models of organizational structure, funding, management, services or staffing. The resources of local societies varied from ideal and well planned - for example purpose-built premises - to minimal resources and/or totally inappropriate accommodation. Most of the services had never been formally evaluated and the philosophy behind the activities of many of them rested on a traditional model where:

> Hard-pressed secretaries are occupied with arranging the socials ... and [do] not have any time for one-to-one help that will make a big difference to a person's life ... for instance a visit to the optician; a repair to a wheelchair ... Real consumer reactions and attitudes have rarely been tested.

As well as highlighting how the success and survival of a local organization was often dependent upon the charisma and sheer hard work of the local secretary or key administrator, Lomas and Vaughan argued that the committees and volunteers with whom they worked might be resistant to changes and developments in their organization, despite the

35

changing needs and characteristics of visually impaired people. The authors also found that new volunteers tended to be recruited through what the local organizations themselves described as 'the old boy network', perhaps reflecting and sustaining a rather static outlook. Although most had difficulties in recruiting help, few organizations approached a volunteer recruitment agency such as the Retired Executives Action Clearing House (REACH).

Notwithstanding an impression that some societies might be unwilling or unable to respond to changing needs and ideas, Lomas and Vaughan documented the continuing ability of such voluntary organizations to attract a high level of financial support from the public, for example in the form of legacies and fund-raising projects:

> Most other charities do not compare ... It confirms that blind welfare still has strong claims on the public's conscience.

However, voluntary organizations for visually impaired people appeared to make less use of grant aid from local authorities than did other charities.

Whilst acknowledging exceptions, Lomas and Vaughan formed the impression of a slow decline in the activities of local voluntary organizations in the face of the growth of social services departments, identifying a mismatch in mutual expectations between them:

> The voluntary workers see the constant shifting of town hall departmental arrangements. The social services staff see too little long-term thinking among most of the societies. In very few cases is there a partnership of equals.

The Partially Sighted Society appeared to be making a significant contribution to the development of services relevant to the needs of visually impaired people in general. In conjunction with representatives of health and social services authorities in South Devon and other relevant local and national voluntary organizations, the PSS had recently produced a report on a study entitled *Services for People With a Visual Impairment* [1A(c)6]. This saw progress in the development of appropriate services for the client group as dependent upon co-operation and co-ordination between the health and social services in particular, but also between local voluntary organizations.

The PSS had played a major role in actually developing low vision services in the geographical area concerned and provided 'a comprehensive functional assessment and low vision training programme to complement the conventional clinical service'. Its report argued that the only way a comprehensive rehabilitation service can be developed effectively is by putting into effect an inter-disciplinary model of service delivery:

> In other words the various professions involved in providing

services for visually impaired people are all seen as being of equal importance to the overall objective of minimising the disabling effect of the impairment.

Whilst the report acknowledged that in some respects such a model of service delivery is more costly in time terms at the assessment stages, the anticipated improvement in the level of rehabilitation which could be obtained would in all probability reduce spending on services in such areas as residential care.

The nature of this particular project was such that it effectively spans the three sub-sections of this first main group of reported studies. It was certainly a review of service organization, and one drawing extensively on users' views; it also represented an evaluation of a service initiative.

Client based surveys of need

Like the last study discussed in the previous sub-section, the first project considered here bridges the rough three-way division of Section 1. Collins' study (Partially Sighted Society), published as *The Clients' View* [1B(c)1], examined the assessments made by visually impaired people in five counties of the services they received. Collins found that people lacked adequate information about services which could help them, that staff had little knowledge of low vision strategies, and that:

> ... vision substitution services are offered more frequently than services for vision enhancement.

Echoing the Shore Report (1985) [1A(c)3], Collins' respondents also identified a low level of counselling services.

With the noteworthy exceptions discussed in the previous sub-section, some of which combined a survey of users' views with other material, most of the general surveys or reviews reported by voluntary organizations had tended to focus directly on people with sight problems as the major subject of study, rather than on existing services and organizational structures. This was true, for example, of the survey of need carried out in Hampshire [1B(c)3], and the similar work being conducted at the time in Cambridgeshire [1B(o)5] and around Chester [1B(o)6]. Generally speaking, these surveys involved postal questionnaires or direct interviews, and aimed to identify the felt needs of existing or potential service users. The further or underlying aim was to seek to have these felt needs reflected in actual provision by directing the results at managers in local social and health services and in other statutory agencies. In some cases voluntary bodies were appraising the help which they or their fellow organizations offered.

Like the reviews of service organization and strategy based largely in local authorities, discussed in the previous sub-section, these surveys of need, largely undertaken by voluntary bodies, mainly sampled local populations, usually essentially within the geographical area defined in the terms of reference of the organization concerned. The RNIB's *General Needs Survey* [1B(o)2], due to be published in 1991, was a national sample survey, building upon the *OPCS Surveys of Disability in Great Britain* (1988 and 1989). As such it was seeking to provide a coherent view of the needs of people with varying degrees and forms of visual impairment, noting as a major limitation of earlier voluntary and statutory sector studies considerable variations in method, content and emphasis, making direct comparison or summation difficult (Bruce and McKennell, 1986).

In 1984, the Research Centre for the Education of the Visually Handicapped, based in the School of Education at the University of Birmingham, had undertaken a pilot survey of the needs and knowledge of available services of blind people in Birmingham (Tobin and Hill, 1984). Its main findings confirmed those of the Shore Report (1985) [1A(c)3]: the majority of the visually impaired people surveyed were elderly and were receiving only minimal rehabilitation services. A larger and more intensive survey had since been developed by the RCEVH. *The Elders Project* [1B(o)1] was a 'longitudinal enquiry ... concerned with the skills and needs of visually handicapped people aged 60 years and above'. It was envisaged that the findings would assist social services departments to target their resources for visually impaired elderly people more effectively. In particular, it aimed to provide information for identifying the training required for work with elderly people with sight problems.

The study by the Bristol Royal Society for the Blind on transport facilities for visually impaired people [1B(c)2] addressed local issues, but its proposals appeared to be of wider possible interest. Little information was yet available on the same organization's ongoing project *Prevention of Blindness: An Examination of Changing Patterns of Care and the Impact on Sight Loss* [1B(o)3].

Evaluations of service initiatives

As we have already remarked, a good deal of interesting local development work was clearly going on in the visual impairment field. However, most of it, unfortunately, was not being subjected to systematic evaluation. In this (sub-)section only two projects which may be termed 'evaluated service initiatives' are listed, neither of them directly involving a social services department. Nor, in general, did social services departments appear to be using research to identify, examine and disseminate examples of good practice. A small number of other projects, for example some primarily concerned with employment or with the needs of special groups, could be seen as 'evaluations of service initiatives'; these are listed in the

Directory in the appropriate section, but also noted in its preceding Contents as 'also relevant to Section 1C'.

Operation Cataract [1C(c)1] was the only example reported of an evaluated attempt to combine the resources of the health sector, the voluntary sector and the private sector. The scheme sought to provide a cheaper alternative to hospital inpatient care and to reduce the waiting list for cataract removal. It was:

> ... co-funded by the South West Thames Regional Health Authority and donations from the voluntary sector mobilised by the Impact Foundation. The final unit cost was £431 per patient.

Surgeons at the West Sussex Eye Unit selected patients from their waiting lists who could be treated as day patients and would be fit enough for post-operative care at a local hotel, taken over for this purpose. Medical and qualified nursing staff provided appropriate pre- and post-operative health care; hotel staff provided domestic support services; the WRVS provided clerical, reception, entertainment and social care services to the patients whilst they were in the hotel, and the British Red Cross Society, Rotary and other community organizations assisted with transport for those who required it.

The project was deemed a success, with the Impact Foundation presenting it as 'a dramatic demonstration of cost-effectiveness'. It appeared to support the claim that waiting lists could be reduced by caring for the more able patients in the manner indicated, and to demonstrate that several agencies - statutory and voluntary - could co-operate and integrate their services to provide necessary care. The results were said to indicate that a shorter recovery period than the five-night stay selected for the project might be feasible. In considering the extension of this model of care, it should be noted that the cost savings in relation to NHS or private inpatient treatment were to a significant extent due to the contribution - a form of 'hidden funding' - of the voluntary organizations.

Some of the reports received in respect of projects listed in sub-sections 1A and 1B recommended a social work contribution being available at eye hospitals and clinics, to assist in the early provision of appropriate help. The second project listed in the present sub-section, the Brighton Society for the Blind's *Evaluation of the Role of an Adviser/Counsellor at an Eye Hospital* [1C(o)1], was looking specifically at the need for such a service, which in this case was being provided by a voluntary organization. The rather wider study of *The Registration and Continuing Care of People with a Visual Impairment* [1A(c)4], reported by Bristol Royal Society for the Blind, was, as noted above, actually undertaken by the social work team manager based at Bristol Eye Hospital.

4 Low vision/partial sight, mobility, training

Low vision/partial sight

Studies specifically concerning low vision or partial sight have been grouped in explicit recognition of the fact that the majority of visually impaired people retain some degree of sight. For the same reason, services to meet the needs of partially sighted people have been emphasized in recent years as one of the most important areas for development.

The projects discussed in the previous chapter essentially addressed in various ways the general range of needs associated with visual impairment and services to meet them. The studies concerned were mainly submitted by local authorities and voluntary organizations. In contrast, the three groups of studies discussed in this chapter - those listed in Sections 2, 3 and 4 of the Directory - are more narrowly focused. Typically, but not exclusively, they had been or were being carried out by academic research centres or by other specialized bodies. No local authorities reported research specifically relating to the needs of or services for people with low vision, in the field of mobility as such, or into the training of specialist workers or of visually impaired people themselves. Acknowledging the valuable work of the Partially Sighted Society, only two other voluntary organizations reported studies in these areas.

Some caution is needed here, since this is in part a terminological matter. The work listed in other categories, not least in Section 1, is relevant to and in one sense encompasses people with low vision/partial sight. However, perceptions of the make-up of the visually impaired population and of the nature of appropriate provision to meet the needs of members of it are important in themselves, and have been called into question; specific attention to low vision is both appropriate and necessary. On the other hand, the apparent lack of local authority research attention specifically to the needs of people with partial sight does not imply that no services were or are being provided for this group. Reported studies indicated the contributions of organizations such as the Partially Sighted Society and the Bristol Royal Society for the Blind, in active collaboration with local authorities, both in research and service provision.

Relatedly, and keeping in view our broad concern with social care, literature searches and direct contacts indicated that the incidence, causes, prevention and treatment of diseases resulting in reduced vision formed the subject matter of a wide range of studies in clinical medicine. However, whilst we were alert to the possible implications of such research for social rehabilitation, and to the issues at the health/social care interface concerning referral and the collaborative provision of support services, our review identified no studies located in 'academic medicine' or in a health service context addressing these topics. The interdependence of medical research, technological innovation, and social care was succinctly identified and described by Collins (1987).

The body of work reported by the Blind Mobility Research Unit, based in the Department of Psychology at the University of Nottingham, represents the most substantial contribution to our overall listing made by a single agency. In introducing Part II of this book it was observed that because the overall classification of projects was designed to best organize the whole body of work identified, many of the studies reported by specialist academic research bodies, in particular the BMRU, fit less easily into the broad categories employed than do most of those emanating from local authorities or voluntary organizations. This is largely because of the greater analytic specification of subject matter and the limited attention to service planning and delivery issues which together characterize the more academic research, particularly where the projects included were part of a long term programme. Projects based in social services departments and voluntary agencies were often of a somewhat general and superficial nature, with their focus given by local relevance in terms of geographical boundaries. Where they had a more specific subject matter, this often reflected an *ad hoc* interest in a particular service at a particular time.

At any one time during the period reviewed, the BMRU's ongoing programme contained a number of precisely defined projects, grouped according to broader themes within the overall subject area (BMRU, 1989). Among the Unit's submissions for our Directory were fundamental psychological studies, some apparently of a unique kind, concerning both the objective and the subjective dimensions of low vision. The Unit's work was emphasizing that residual vision is itself to be regarded as an aid in the context of mobility and other activities: an important point to make in relation to some conventional perspectives on 'blindness'. Much of the Unit's more fundamental work has by its very nature been at some remove from immediate practical application. However, it has had and retains the capacity to be widely influential, particularly given the linkage in the Unit's programme between understanding the mobility skills and difficulties of people with sight problems, by means *inter alia* of 'task analysis', and identifying the appropriate methods and contents of training for both specialist workers and people with sight problems themselves. The theme of 'assessment' is also central in this context; in particular the acknowledged need to develop adequate methods and measures for people with low vision, suited to specific forms and aspects of visual impairment and relevant to the performance of a range of daily living and other tasks.

The close inter-linking of the BMRU work categorized here as primarily concerning 'low vision/partial sight' (Section 2 of the Directory), 'mobility' (Section 3), or 'training ...' (Section 4), is indicated in the titles of the relevant projects. The Unit's work on mobility, whether fundamental or more practical, has been treated as the core of its programme for the purposes of offering a descriptive account. The 'mobility projects' interweave with much of the work focusing on low vision as such, and these two bodies of work together underpin the Unit's specific studies on training and assessment. Given the purposes of our review, the more detailed discussion of the Unit's work therefore appears under 'mobility' and 'training'. This is consistent with the greatest number of individual project entries from the BMRU being in Section 3, with the next largest group in Section 4 and the least number of projects in the 'low vision' section. However, considerable cross-referencing is necessary in this discussion, just as the Directory itself has extensive lists of (BMRU) projects 'also relevant to this section' in each of Sections 2, 3 and 4.

Two BMRU projects are given their main entries in Section 2. In *The Development of Measures of Low Vision Mobility Performance* [2(c)1], Dodds used video analysis to measure differences in mobility between partially sighted people who had received training and those who had not. In a related experiment, *Low Vision Assessment and Training* [4(c)4], Dodds and colleagues developed computer based visual assessment training tasks. Repeated practice was shown to improve performance, which could be transferred to real life mobility. The measures involved could also be used as a better system of performance prediction than acuity data. The subjects in the first experiment were partially sighted people, and in the second registered blind and partially sighted people.

In *Motion Vision in the Partially Sighted* [2(o)2] and other projects, Doyle and colleagues were using computer based technology to advance the understanding of the mobility of partially sighted people, to develop assessments of motion vision, and thence to identify training needs. They were also using a 'swinging room' (*Visual Balance Control* [3(o)7]), and investigating the validity of training partially sighted people under a blindfold in order to develop their skills in audio location (*Obstacle Location Without Vision* [3(o)3]). The subjects for this latter project were sighted university undergraduates, and for the 'swinging room' experiments mainly undergraduates or sixth formers. However, partially sighted people were to be included in the computer based project.

Beggs had identified that loss of the lower peripheral field is particularly important in relation to the mobility of people with low vision. In his *Investigation of Mobility Officers' Assessments of Clients' Needs for Training* [4(c)3], he concluded that the training of mobility officers had not until recently equipped them to analyse objectively the specific mobility problems experienced by partially sighted people.

Work led by Beggs (*Task Analysis of Mobility* [3(o)5]) and Dodds (*Psychological Adjustment to Sight Loss* [4(o)3]) was exploring how personality factors, psychological disposition, and intellectual skills influence the extent to which a visually impaired person responds to mobility training. The subjective experiences of partially sighted people in the specific contexts of mobility and training represented another important element in BMRU's overall research programme. Relevant projects, for example [3(c)2], [3(o)2], [4(o)2] and [4(o)3], are discussed later.

We have already noted the national role of the Partially Sighted Society in promoting and developing services for people with low vision. Some of its research and service development contributions - of a rather different kind to those of the BMRU - were discussed in Chapter 3. For example, Collins' study [1B(c)1] revealed a lack of knowledge among direct service providers, such that:

> vision substitution services are offered more frequently than services for vision enhancement.

In the inter-disciplinary context of the South Devon Review and Planning Group, a comprehensive rehabilitation service was being developed [1A(c)6]. The Partially Sighted Society's *Evaluation of Task Lighting* [2(c)2] examined the efficacy of various light bulbs for partially sighted people. The Society was also undertaking an *Evaluation of a Low Vision Training Programme* [4(o)2], the initiative concerned being aimed at people suffering from macular degeneration, one of the commonest causes of sight loss amongst elderly people.

The other voluntary organization reporting work examining low vision services was Bristol Royal Society for the Blind. In its review of *Low Vision Services in Avon* [2(o)1] it, like the South Devon Review and Planning Group [1A(c)6], was exploring a multidisciplinary approach.

Mobility

Mobility is generally seen as the key to personal freedom and normality for visually impaired people, and thus as one of the most important aspects of rehabilitation. It was therefore neither surprising nor inappropriate that work related to mobility, particularly concerning mobility training for people with a visual impairment and the training of the specialist workers who provide such training, should feature so prominently in recent research related to the needs of the client group. The Blind Mobility Research Unit had been working in these areas since 1966; its constantly evolving programme had yielded a much greater body of publications than is listed or discussed here. Even more than Section 2 of the Directory, the group of studies listed in Section 3 is dominated by the BMRU's work. No research which could be regarded as specifically focusing on mobility was reported by social services departments; nor did we identify any such work in health service contexts. Only one project based in a voluntary organization was reported: a study concerned with mobility aids [3(o)1].

A survey on the mobility habits of visually impaired people who had received mobility training, carried out in Nottingham before the period covered by our review, had revealed few if any measurable changes over the fifteen years since such training had been introduced (Clark-Carter et al., 1981). Significant components of BMRU's subsequent work reflected concerns stemming from this study, with attempts made to analyse the tasks and the related experiences involved when visually impaired people walk and travel. The studies reported suggested that the Unit had developed a particular, but not exclusive, emphasis on the mobility problems and needs of partially sighted rather than totally blind people. Themes included how mobility training is experienced by its recipients, and a continuing concern with the nature, quality and style of the assessment and training offered to and by specialist workers. This work both had a practical orientation towards training, and was informed by fundamental theoretical and empirical work on motivation.

In much of BMRU's research, experimental methods have been employed to examine specifically defined methods and objectives. Relatively small samples have been used, most but not all of whose members have been visually impaired. Psychological models and techniques have been used to identify personality characteristics, attitudes and coping skills in relation to mobility training and other forms of rehabilitation. 'Task analysis' has frequently formed part of the research design. The potential for the findings to be applied in the context of rehabilitation programmes with other disabled groups remains apparent.

Those reported BMRU projects most explicitly related to training are discussed in the next section. Here the focus is mainly upon the Unit's work in seeking to understand the tasks and experiences of mobility. The most relevant listed studies include *Investigation of Mobility Related Feelings* [3(c)2], *Task Analysis of Mobility* [3(o)5], *Preliminary Comparison of Expert and Poor Travellers' Abilities to Cope With Independent Travel* [3(o)4], and *Mobility*

44

Related Feelings and the Walking Speed of Visually Impaired Travellers [3(o)2]. 'Mobility related feelings' was an important research theme at the BMRU, where '[a model had been built] of how clients feel when undertaking a journey' (Beggs, 1989b, pp. 12-14). Three important aspects of personality functioning were under continuing exploration. The first was 'self-efficacy' (Dodds, 1989): a sense of competency in the face of the threat and anxiety which travelling arouses in a visually impaired person. The second was the 'cognitive arousal factor': 'visually impaired travel is perceived as difficult, and dangerous, and therefore needs a person's full attention'. The third was 'role acceptance': 'the embarrassment of being seen as a cane user'. The researchers' hypothesis was that successful mobility training would enhance self-efficacy, reduce cognitive arousal, and help people adjust to a new role. The management of anxiety had emerged as an important ability for the visually impaired person to possess or develop, with 'competency enhancement' therefore an important aspect of the teaching style required of specialist instructors.

Also of relevance under a 'mobility' heading, Dodds and Hellawell were continuing their studies of spatial perception, for example in relation to the use of tactile maps, which visually impaired people, mobility instructors, and teachers of children with sight loss had not necessarily found usable (*Spatial Representation and Congenital Blindness* [3(c)4]). Related work was being carried out at Sheffield University on the *Use of Maps and Graphics in the Mobility Training of Young Visually Handicapped Children* [3(o)6].

Dodds and Hellawell were also conducting experiments in auditory awareness with naïve subjects and skilled blind travellers. The aim of this work was to be able to produce teaching tapes to train visually impaired people to understand and use sound to enhance their mobility skills (Dodds and Hellawell, 1989, pp. 11-12). The development and use by Doyle and others of a 'swinging room' (*Visual Balance Control* [3(o)7]), and the same group's investigations of the validity of training partially sighted people under a blindfold in order to develop their skills in audio location (*Obstacle Location Without Vision* [3(o)3]), were referred to above.

The reported BMRU work was particularly sensitive to the fact that most visually impaired people are not blind but rather have various types and degrees of partial sight, and to the importance of encouraging and helping people to maximize their ability to use their residual vision as a mobility aid. However, the Unit's research was implicitly taking as its target client group adults of normal intelligence whose mobility problems were essentially a product of sight loss and their feelings about this, rather than reflecting other or additional physical or mental disabilities. The BMRU projects reported to us did not directly address the additional mobility problems which may be experienced by visually impaired people who are elderly, who have additional, non-sensory, physical disabilities, severe learning difficulties, or who may also be suffering from a hearing loss. However, the mobility training of these groups had been discussed by

BMRU staff, for example by Dodds in *Multi-handicap, low vision and the teaching of mobility* (1985) and *Mobility Training For Visually Handicapped People: A Person-Centred Approach* (1988).

Training of specialist staff, and assessment and training of visually impaired people

Along with - and often directly involving - the specific topic area of mobility, the training of specialist workers and (thereby) of visually impaired people themselves could be said at the time of our review to have dominated recent social research in the field, including that funded by the Department of Health. This was not inappropriate, since training for those involved with the rehabilitation of visually impaired people was and remains an absolutely central issue of both policy and practice. The link between 'training the trainers' and providing appropriate rehabilitative training for visually impaired people themselves is sufficient rationale for uniting these themes in the Directory and in this discussion.

A brief historical summary of the development of training for specialist workers appears in *A Wider Vision* (SSI, 1988b). The Department of Health had more recently funded a further major study in this area, entitled *Training for Workers in Visual Impairment* [4(c)7]. This was undertaken by the National Foundation for Educational Research (NFER) and published as *Beyond Vision* (Maychell and Smart, 1990). The training of specialist staff and the assessment and training of visually impaired people was also a theme of the continuing work of the BMRU, whose core funding represented another significant proportion of Department of Health support for research related to visual impairment during the period reviewed.

The other of the two main University based centres in this field, namely the Research Centre for the Education of the Visually Handicapped at Birmingham, had recently undertaken research on the training of visually impaired adults, albeit with a different emphasis. If BMRU's basic focus in this context could be said to have been on mobility, that of RCEVH had been on communication skills, though in neither case exclusively so. Work at Sheffield University on the mobility and orientation training of young visually impaired children [3(o)6], ongoing at the time of our review, is also relevant here.

Academically based research centres thus appeared to be the major current contributors in respect of studies related to the training of specialist staff and to the assessment and training of visually impaired people themselves. We received no indication that any social services departments had been or were undertaking research in these areas, but two studies based in the voluntary sector are included in this sub-section ([4(o)2] and [4(o)5]). Mobility training as such was of course being offered by the Guide Dogs for the Blind Association and by universities and colleges training teachers of visually impaired children, but no research was reported by these bodies.

We shall discuss the research listed in Section 4 under three headings: 'fundamental research with training implications', 'assessment of the specialist training courses', and 'other specific studies'.

Fundamental research with training implications

The BMRU work listed in Section 4, much of which is also relevant under the categories of 'mobility' and 'low vision', has several linked dimensions: an understanding of client motivation which acknowledges the psychological underpinnings of performance, including personality factors and coping strategies, and which encompasses the expectations and feelings of visually impaired people in the context of rehabilitation, particularly mobility training; the identification and analysis of the numerous tasks involved in mobility; and the detailed analysis and evaluation of the work of specialist trainers.

The psychological models, assessment tools and teaching styles being developed at the BMRU were seen as challenging the understanding and practice rooted in a 'loss model' of visual impairment (BMRU, 1989; Dodds, 1989). They also embodied the concept of 'starting where the client is' and extended the Rogerian concept of empathy (Beggs, 1989a, pp. 17-18). An attempt was being made to devise models and styles of training for mobility officers which were more sensitive to clients' situations than had been the case in the past (Beggs, 1985), and which were also of a more structured nature, and to evaluate them in terms of outcomes. 'Task analysis' was a key part of the approach being adopted. It was being used to identify and specify the elements of the actual skills necessary to perform a practical task. It was also being employed in respect of the tasks involved in teaching these skills. All of this work appeared capable of much wider application in the rehabilitation field as a whole, including in work with other client groups. It also seemed generally relevant to staff training in a variety of health and welfare fields.

Some of the individual BMRU projects reported addressed 'both sides' of the teacher/learner interaction in the practical context of mobility training. They were underpinned by past and current studies seeking to understand the tasks and experiences of mobility (e.g. *Task Analysis of Mobility* [3(o)5] and *Investigation of Mobility Related Feelings* [3(c)2]), and work aiming to develop appropriate assessment tools, especially for partially sighted people (e.g. *The Development of Measures of Low Vision Mobility Performance* [2(c)1] and *Low Vision Assessment and Training* [4(c)4]).

Dodds et al.'s *Psychological Adjustment to Sight Loss* [4(o)3] was exploring the impact on rehabilitative outcomes of attitudinal and personality problems. Beggs' *Investigation of Mobility Officers' Assessments of Clients' Needs for Training* [4(c)3] identified that the training of mobility officers had not until recently equipped them to analyse objectively the specific mobility problems experienced by partially sighted people. Beggs' *Role Play of Different Training Styles* [4(c)6] confirmed earlier work on the differential psychological benefit of mobility officers' teaching styles in relation to learning. Adult visually impaired people were found to be more likely to prefer non-directive or 'egalitarian' styles of teaching to the more directive teaching techniques used in the past, including in the training of mobility officers themselves (Beggs, 1985; Dodds, 1988). The researchers suggested that the differential effectiveness of teaching styles is related to the fact that visually impaired people wish to take responsibility for their own travel skills at different paces, and to whether or not they are enabled and encouraged to explore with their instructors the problems encountered in developing their mobility skills.

Assessment of the specialist training courses

The NFER study *Training For Workers in Visual Impairment* [4(c)7], commissioned by the Department of Health and published as *Beyond Vision* (Maychell and Smart, 1990), provided a comprehensive analysis of the content and nature of a number of specialist training programmes. The courses mainly concerned were those for mobility officers offered by the National Mobility Centre (NMC), the North Regional Association for the Blind (NRAB), and the South Regional Association for the Blind (SRAB), and those for technical officers provided by the NRAB and the SRAB.[1] The researchers also examined the characteristics of the students and their subsequent work and working environments.

The study sought to clarify how these training programmes, based in the voluntary sector, related to the needs of the client group and to the ultimate service task - the majority of specialist workers being employed within local authority social services departments. The report suggested changes in the style and content of the courses in order that they might reflect more adequately both the needs of visually impaired people and specialist workers' employment contexts. The issue underlying the first was the changing demographic profile of the visually impaired population, in terms of age, the patterning as between various eye disorders, and consequent rehabilitation needs. Behind the second lay the changing policy, organizational, and resource contexts of social services departments.

The NFER researchers interviewed staff of the training agencies and past and present students. They observed some of the teaching in progress and examined course documentation, developing a detailed description and analysis of the content of each course. They had direct contact with the total student group for 1986 and conducted a postal survey of a sample of previously trained workers about the relevance of their training to their employment experience. A sub-sample of case studies of work experience in six locations was also included in their report.

Whilst some of the comments of former and current students were specific to the content or staffing of their particular course, common critical themes emerged concerning all three courses. Both the qualified workers and the current students commented on:

> ... an overwhelming emphasis on students learning the skills themselves, as opposed to learning how to transmit the skills to clients.

It had long been an assumption on these courses that students should be assessed on the expertise which they themselves developed in mobility and daily living skills under blindfolds or with vision impairment simulation spectacles.

Respondents also identified an assumption in their courses that the people they worked with would be highly motivated to acquire new skills; workers had had no preparation in responding to people who were not interested in receiving training. Respondents had found that the interest shown by visually impaired people in rehabilitation may be affected by the extent to which they have already developed their own strategies of adaptation; others may simply have very limited aspirations, perhaps because of advanced age.

The BMRU's conceptual and empirical work, 'unpacking' motivation (Dodds, 1989) and analysing the tasks of mobility and of training with the aim of enabling specialist workers to structure their understanding of their clients, is clearly relevant here. Both the Department of Health (*A Wider Vision* (SSI, 1988b)) and the BMRU (1989) have argued that for training purposes the loss model of adjustment is too limited to account fully for the behaviour, needs, or potential ways of helping visually impaired people. Dodds, Gaskell and Hellawell (1989, pp. 3-5) suggest that visually impaired people experience a variety of feelings about themselves which reflect the way their personalities functioned prior to acquiring their impairment, as well as its subsequent impact on their attitudes and life-style. They also suggest that a visually impaired person's perceived social support and general health status should be part of the specialist worker's assessment agenda when considering a response to the offer of training. Poor health, inadequate support, or discouraging attitudes on the part of significant others can undermine confidence and interest in improving mobility.

Counselling skills were identified as a training need by both the qualified workers and the students who took part in the NFER study, echoing the recognition of visually impaired people's counselling needs in *A Wider Vision* (SSI, 1988b). The latter advocated a 'whole person' approach, and viewed counselling as part of this. The NFER researchers found that the training centres had been reluctant to offer counselling on their courses until recently, perhaps reflecting the use of a 'skills-centred' as opposed to a 'person-centred' model of training (Dodds, 1988).

The NFER's respondents also felt that they needed much more training specifically to meet the particular needs of partially sighted people. Some tutors were seen as assuming or implying that skills techniques appropriate for totally blind people can be adapted easily for use with people with low vision. Past and present students found that helping the latter group was much more complex than this would imply, echoing Collins' study of rehabilitation services [1B(c)1] and the assumptions behind the BMRU's more recent low vision projects [2(o)2], [3(o)7]. The latter were seeking to identify the useful residual sight of partially sighted people in order to assess the likelihood of their benefiting from mobility training. The NFER report suggested that work specifically on low vision should form a major part of the training of rehabilitation workers.

Finally, the NFER study suggested a need for better and more appropriate preparation of students for their future employment contexts, particularly for working in social services departments. The qualified workers and students reported experiencing the structure and organization of social services departments as complex and hard to understand. They also often found themselves professionally isolated, and felt undervalued and unsupported, both within their own agencies and by others they contacted on behalf of their clients'.

A Wider Vision (SSI, 1988b) identified as management tasks for social services departments a number of the issues highlighted as training tasks by the respondents in the NFER study. Departments were recommended to review their organizational structures with a view to countering the isolation experienced by specialist workers and the low status felt both by them and by their clients, to improve their assessment and planning functions, and to examine and improve their mechanisms of accountability in order to raise the standards of staff supervision and support. These measures would, said the SSI, improve the quality of services available to people with sight loss.

The problem of the low status accorded to some professionals working with visually impaired people by other professionals in the same field was among the issues being addressed by the South Devon Review and Planning Group's inter-disciplinary development work [1A(c)6].

Like *A Wider Vision*, the NFER report drew attention to the 'backwater' status of specialist services for visually impaired people, following the establishment (in 1971) of unified departments of (personal) social services within local authorities. NFER's historical account of the period indicates that the titles of the courses and of the qualifications offered by the training agencies changed several times. There have been various discussions over the years about accreditation, but at the time of our review this area of professional training remained outside mainstream social work education.[2]

In 1985, the NRAB began to offer a training course for rehabilitation officers, seeking to combine the two previous qualifications for mobility and technical officers. In 1987 and 1988 the SRAB and the NMC also started 'rehabilitation worker' courses, with the similar objective of providing 'a unified form of qualifying training for specialist workers with the visually handicapped' and with similar content to the NRAB course.[3]

Most of the NFER analysis was in fact based on the views of students and qualified workers who trained *before* these new courses commenced, but the report included an update on the differences between the old and the new courses. The new training programmes included topics reflecting the changing needs of the visually impaired population. The time devoted to assessment and teaching skills, counselling, and the organizational nature of the social services departments had been increased. The time spent on training under blindfolds or learning Braille had been reduced and the time available to develop low vision skills and knowledge increased. In practice, however, the contents and approaches of the new courses were said already to have begun to diverge. Different selection procedures were evident, different kinds of staff were employed to teach the students, differing amounts of time allocated to the jointly agreed topics, and different procedures adopted for the final assessment of the students. Continuing variations amongst the training agencies appeared to echo the variable standards in the field identified by the SSI in *A Wider Vision* (SSI, 1988b).

Dodds, Hellawell and Gaskell (BMRU) had examined the specific client assessment procedures being developed at the RNIB Employment Rehabilitation Centre at Torquay [4(c)1]. The purpose of this study was to identify objective criteria and eventually to develop assessment systems capable of singling out as early as possible those clients who will not benefit from vocational training. The methods of assessment being developed included vocational assessment tests, staff assessments based on predetermined criteria, and 'psychological tests which are able to measure aspects of a client's state of mind and general morale, relevant to rehabilitation'. The report on this exercise was not available for external circulation; the researchers involved stressed that the work was very new.

Other specific studies related to training

The Research Centre for the Education of the Visually Handicapped (RCEVH), based in the School of Education at the University of Birmingham, reported several completed or ongoing projects for inclusion in our review. They shared as their common thread the examination of the impact of sight loss on adults, and the various forms of training which can be developed to overcome or compensate for this. Reflecting the criteria set out in Chapter 2, examples of that part of the Centre's work closely related to the formal education of visually impaired children have not been included. Nor has detailed attention been given to the Centre's important developmental work on the many valuable aids based on new technology. In *The Manual Dexterity of Visually Handicapped Adults* [4(c)5], the RCEVH developed an experimental model to assess the effect of differing levels of sight loss on the manual dexterity of men and women below retirement age. Females were found generally to have greater manual dexterity than males, with the degree of residual vision possessed by subjects being another important variable. We noted earlier the prominence given in the BMRU's work on the response of visually impaired people to mobility training to the nature and degree of residual vision available: for example in projects [4(c)3], [2(c)1] and [4(c)4]. The BMRU had not, however, emphasized the sex or gender of subjects as a significant factor.

The RCEVH was developing objective tests capable of conveying specific information to people outside the academic field, such as placement officers, trainers and potential employers. These evaluative procedures were also seen as providing a framework for generating comparative data on the performance of visually impaired people before and after receiving training, and for information about:

> ... willingness to use any residual vision; motivation and teachability; relative superiority of the right hand over the left (or vice versa); and general speed, mode of attack and approach to problem solving.

Many of these topics echo the research which was being pursued by the BMRU in its exploration of the concept of motivation, the feelings of people about their visual impairment, and the significance of these for their response to training. The RCEVH's subjects in the research into manual dexterity included people with normal sight, so that the impact of sight loss could be more directly observed.

The findings from *The Elders Project* [1B(o)1] were seen as likely to provide information for identifying the training required for work with elderly visually impaired people. The studies entitled *Using Sighted Volunteers for Teaching Moon to Newly Blinded Adults* [4(o)4] and *Access to Information and Learning by Visually Handicapped People Through Micro-Computer Technology* [4(o)1] were also relevant to training issues.

The students and qualified workers interviewed by the NFER researchers found that acquiring the skill to use Braille themselves was very time-consuming, that it required proper training to be able to teach Braille effectively to others, and that in fact only a minority of newly registered people ever wished to learn it. Tobin and Hill (RCEVH) suggested that because Moon more closely resembles the printed alphabet it can be read by sighted people as well as scanned easily by touch by visually impaired people. They therefore felt that it should be possible to train sighted volunteers to teach Moon to newly blinded adults and argued that this would have several beneficial effects, for example: providing social contact in the local community for visually impaired people, maintaining their literacy skills, and freeing rehabilitation workers for other training tasks.

Embodied in *Access to Information and Learning by Visually Handicapped*

People Through Micro-Computer Technology [4(o)1] was the aim of:

... produc[ing] micro-computer software that will allow blind and partially sighted people of all ages to have access to the same information as their fully sighted peers.

Training specialist workers to train visually impaired people to use computers was not part of the course structure of the training agencies.[4] Visually impaired people receiving such training were most likely to be in full-time education, whether at school, college or university, or to be attending particular vocational training programmes.

The detailed examination of research and development work in the rapidly growing field of electronic aids was outside our brief and expertise. However, the potential of such equipment for enhancing and maintaining the independence of visually impaired people cannot be over-estimated; it was clear that training in its use, and teaching others to use it, would have to be incorporated into rehabilitation workers' courses.

Two projects based in voluntary organizations feature among those in this section of our listing. One, Surrey Voluntary Association for the Blind's *Welfare of the Visually Impaired: Daily Living Skills and Independence* [4(o)5], appeared to have a similar focus to the RCEVH's *Elders Project* [1B(o)1].

The Partially Sighted Society's *Evaluation of a Low Vision Training Programme* [4(o)2] is of considerable interest, with potential direct benefits for visually impaired people and implications for the development of training for specialist workers. The project, ongoing at the time of our review, was an experiment attempting to help elderly sufferers from macular degeneration, one of the most common sight disorders of advanced age, to maximize the use of their residual vision and thus maintain their independence. The project involved training clients to use 'eccentric fixation' and the PSS expected to complete it in May 1992.

These two projects, along with the RNIB's *General Needs Survey* [1B(o)2] and the RCEVH's *Elders Project* [1B(o)1], exemplify growing recognition of the numerical predominance, within the overall client group, of elderly people, generally with varying degrees of acquired sight difficulties, and a consequent reduction in the proportion who are younger and literally blind - whether from birth or through later trauma.

Notes

1   There have been changes subsequently, in both the funding and the location of these courses; see Postscript.
2   See Postscript for more up-to-date information.
3   See note 1 and Postscript.
4   It seems unlikely that this remains the situation.

5 Other research

Dual sensory impairment

The previous two chapters, discussing the studies listed in Sections 1 to 4 of the Directory (Appendix), have considered themes relating to visually impaired people in general. This population contains groups with additional or special needs. People with dual sensory impairment - deaf-blind people - are one such minority group, although the term 'minority' must be used with caution. The number of people with a double sensory loss is not known accurately, in part because of the lack of standardization among local authority record systems identifying this group, and in part because the majority of those concerned are elderly. In the latter case they are likely to have acquired their sensory impairments over time and at differing rates, so that these conditions are commonly unrecognized or unacknowledged, both by those suffering from them and by professionals.

Two major national reports on the needs of people with dual sensory impairment appeared in the period shortly before we undertook our review. The first, which has been included in our listing [5(c)1], was *Breaking Through: Developing Services for Deaf-Blind People* (RNIB (Deaf-Blind Services Liaison Group), 1988), the result of joint work between four voluntary organizations - RNIB, RNID, SENSE (the National Deaf-Blind and Rubella Association), and the National Deaf-Blind League. The second, drawing upon and supportive of *Breaking Through*, was *Sign Posts: Leading to Better Social Services for Deaf-Blind People* (SSI, 1989). *Sign Posts* was one of the few reports acquired during our review which was available in large print format.

Although we were able to identify only a small number of research projects on dual sensory loss, it was apparent that *Breaking Through* and *Sign Posts* - perhaps especially the latter, given its source - were having an impact on a number of local authorities and stimulating joint work (including research) on the part of social services departments and voluntary organizations. The emphasis in the studies listed was generally on numbers and needs, rather than on developing and evaluating models of 'good practice'. However, the Department of Health commissioned a project of the latter type [5(o)2] whilst our review was in progress (see below).

A number of the projects listed had recently been completed or were ongoing, and it seemed that further similar work was likely to be undertaken in the near future in other parts of the country. It should also be recalled that since we had neither specifically excluded nor specifically included special needs groups in our advice to potential respondents, complete coverage could not be assumed.

Breaking Through [5(c)1] brought together the available data on the potential size and nature of the population with dual sensory impairment, and argued that the previous lack of such information had led to a failure to develop appropriate services. Similar recommendations were made to those in other relatively recent RNIB and SSI reports: a need to develop a philosophy and strategy of service for this group, to raise standards of assessment, to adopt a multidisciplinary approach to reflect and then to meet need, and to ensure adequate staff training. Specific recommendations were made for particular service areas, for example:

> Social workers should seek to ensure that deaf people have their vision regularly tested, that blind people have their hearing regularly tested, and that any indication of the development of a secondary sensory impairment should result in referral to the appropriate services. (para. 2.4)

> Every Social Services Department should establish a standing Forum for the formation of a comprehensive strategy and plan of action for the furtherance of the welfare of deaf-blind people. (para. 11.4)

Sign Posts (SSI, 1989) was specifically concerned with services for deaf-blind people provided by local authority social services departments. The report was based upon a pilot study and inspection in five authorities; it included the views of some service users and reported discussions with local voluntary organizations. Social services departments' relative failure to recognize the needs of people with dual sensory impairment, and the consequent low level of provision, were strongly criticized. The report's recommendations echoed those of other SSI reports such as *A Wider Vision*

(1988b) and *Say it Again* (1988a).

Some of the work listed in this section predated *Breaking Through*. An example is the study of the *Feasibility of a County-Wide Service for Deaf-Blind People* carried out by Chapman for Norfolk Social Services Department in 1986 [5(c)2]. Chapman's local findings reflected the national picture as reported later. The records of the Authority concerned were felt to be inadequate in terms of identifying the numbers and needs of the client group, and services were said to be underdeveloped.

Chapman recruited and trained guide-helpers for the Authority. Their role was clearly distinguished from those of social workers and of social work assistants. Among Chapman's recommendations was that the Social Services Department should allocate a budget to a particular local voluntary organization to provide and train guide-helpers. He offered guidelines for recruiting the latter and suggested a curriculum for their training.

Chapman produced a valuable guide to assessment, covering many of the points made in *Breaking Through* [5(c)1]. Psycho-social needs should be acknowledged, along with the possible need for a range of professional and voluntary services to be involved, and for:

> ... practical and technical advice on becoming more independent
> in coping with daily living needs ... [and] maximising the safe use
> of residual sight and hearing ...

Being both registered partially sighted and a qualified social worker himself, Chapman's personal experience and understanding of the position of the service user, of the role of social services staff, and of the contribution of voluntary organizations, add considerably to the credibility of this report.

In 1987-88, the Directorate of Housing and Personal Social Services of the London Borough of Bexley conducted a *Review of Services for Hearing Impaired and Visually Handicapped People* [5(c)3]. The report was internal to the Department, with copies only available with the permission of the Director.

Section 5 of the Directory includes five projects which were ongoing at the time of our review. Two of these ([5(o)4] and [5(o)5]) were clearly direct responses to *Breaking Through*; each involved setting up a Standing Forum. Sunderland and Durham County Incorporated Royal Institution for the Blind reported examining *Provision of Services for Deaf-Blind People* [5(o)4] jointly with the local social services department - although the latter sent a 'nil return'. Through its *Review and Survey of the Provision of Services to People who are Deaf-Blind* [5(o)5], the Social Services Division of Stockport Metropolitan Borough Council was seeking to identify the number of people with dual sensory loss in its area and their degrees of impairment, and to share this with other local statutory and voluntary agencies.

Devon Social Services Department had engaged SENSE South West to carry out an extensive survey: *Identifying Needs and Numbers of Deaf-Blind in Devon* [5(o)3]. This was scheduled to be completed by the end of 1990, with the report obtainable from the Local Authority. Bristol Royal Society for the Blind was similarly examining *Deaf-Blind Services in Avon* [5(o)1].

In recognition of the growing importance of this field of special need, the Department of Health commissioned the Hester Adrian Research Centre at the University of Manchester to evaluate the work of SENSE Midlands [5(o)2].

Multiple impairment including sight loss

This special category of projects, like the previous one, brings together studies referring to a particular minority of the total number of people with a substantial sight loss. Again, work specifically in this area was not central to the concerns of our review, especially where the primary diagnosis of the people concerned would be severe learning difficulties. Therefore we have similar reservations to those indicated in the previous section - and for similar reasons - regarding the likely completeness of our listing. However, on the basis of what was reported to us, only Cornwall among local authorities appeared to have undertaken research in this subject area [6(c)2].

Terminology has been somewhat problematic in this field. People with severe learning difficulties form the largest sub-group amongst people with multiple impairments which include sight loss. Probably because of this the term 'multi-handicapped visually impaired' was quite commonly used at the time of our review, to refer to this sub-group alone rather than to all of those people with sight and additional impairments. This was confusing because, like anyone else, visually impaired people can suffer from other kinds of congenital or adventitious impairment. Use of the term 'mental handicap' is widely unacceptable now, but for services to become more relevant to this client group, terminology which explicitly distinguishes their specific interests may be important.

The most significant recent research identified on services for 'multi-handicapped visually impaired people' was conducted for the RNIB [6(c)3] and published as *Out of Isolation* (Best et al., 1987). Its focus was 'the mismatch between the needs of these people and current services'. *Out of Isolation* offered various estimates of the numbers of multiply-impaired people with sight loss (see for example Tables 1 and 2, p. 12, which are drawn from Moss (1985)) and demonstrated the non-homogeneity of the group. The study was part of an RNIB policy development initiative which began in 1985, in recognition of the fact that, in common with the statutory agencies, few of its services were directed towards this particular group. The report identified a number of specific problems, with a relevance for service provision both by and beyond RNIB:

57

- sub-groups are too small and thinly dispersed to develop cost-effective services

- the label of the major disability obscures needs relating to other disabilities

- assessment skills and standards, mobility aids and training, communication skills, low vision enhancement, and accessible information appropriate to the special needs of the group each need developing, along with training to work with the clients concerned

- accommodation represents a particular area of need for people with multiple impairments including sight loss.

Like other RNIB reports produced in the same period, *Out of Isolation* reflected upon the Institute's own future role. It identified a need to build on existing services, and emphasized the potential cost-effectiveness of a regional approach. Many of the specific developmental recommendations in the report have since been implemented, for example a pilot advisory team project and an information and training service.

Out of Isolation made reference to the work of the Committee on the Multi-Handicapped Blind, which was set up with the assistance of SRAB and had been instrumental for several years in promoting the interests of this group of clients. At the time of our review, SRAB was itself undertaking a national survey of *Services for Multi-Handicapped Visually Impaired People* [6(o)1]. Diana Harries, the researcher conducting this study, indicated to us that the results appeared likely to confirm the findings of the OPCS (1988 and 1989) that the numbers involved - and consequently the resources needed for this client group - had thus far generally been underestimated. She suggested that as multiple impairment was much more prevalent than had been generally assumed, agencies seeing themselves as essentially responding to single disabilities should be reflecting on the total needs of the populations to whom they were addressing their services, and adopting a 'whole person approach' to meeting special needs.

Cornwall Social Services Department's report, *Mentally Handicapped People with Hearing and Sight Problems* [6(c)2], arose from a review of the County's mental handicap register. It illustrated how focusing attention on the identification of one form of impairment can mask the identification of needs associated with other impairments. Particular difficulties were noted concerning assessment, registration, and service delivery in rural areas.

Two studies reported by the Bristol Royal Society for the Blind focused on people with learning difficulties and a visual impairment. Both were small-scale projects, funded under the Society's bursary scheme, and both examined current services with a view to improving practice. *Day Care for Visually Impaired People with Learning Difficulties* [6(c)1] highlighted the low numbers identified in the geographical area studied and the lack of staff resources or planned and co-ordinated services to meet their needs. By setting up a trial day care group, the author of the report had been able to identify both the benefits offered by day care and the resources needed. *Visual Assessment at the Wyvern Special Education Centre, Pewsey* [6(c)4] involved developing tests of visual acuity for people without literacy skills. It was found possible to assess the vision of subjects just as effectively using familiar objects such as a cup of tea as with the more standard card and object tests. 'Key workers' were closely involved and through becoming more aware of the level and nature of sight problems amongst the people they were helping were beginning to assess how these difficulties contributed to behaviour problems.

Bristol Royal Society for the Blind had also published *Sensory Impairment and Mental Handicap*, a staff resource pack, in conjunction with staff at Stoke Park Hospital.

Education

The crucial contribution made by education in the broadest sense to the lives of visually impaired people cannot be over-estimated. However, we saw research in the field of formal education as outside our terms of reference (see Chapter 2) and excluded from our review valuable work in this area which came to our notice, much of it concerning resources and techniques to enable visually impaired children to have the same educational opportunities as their sighted peers. Similarly, we also by-and-large excluded the specialized area of communication skills and aids for people with sight problems, including the rapidly expanding and increasingly important application of information technology in this field.

The Research Centre for the Education of the Visually Handicapped (RCEVH), based in the School of Education at the University of Birmingham, has been involved for many years in a wide range of studies relating to the special educational needs of visually impaired people: both adults and children. This work has addressed both formal education and acquiring skills to compensate for the loss or diminution of reading ability. It has ranged from the analysis of teaching techniques, through various projects concerning Braille and Moon, to the development of microcomputer software. The Centre makes available extensive listings of research and other publications in its fields of interest.

There is of course some overlap between formal education, the teaching of skills, including 'life skills', and vocational training, both for young visually impaired people and those suffering impairments in later life, and thus some overlap between Section 7 and other parts of the Directory, especially Section 4. The RCEVH's *Access to Information and Learning by Visually Handicapped People Through Micro-Computer Technology* [4(o)1], *The Manual Dexterity of Visually Handicapped Adults* [4(c)5], and *Using Sighted*

59

Volunteers for Teaching Moon to Newly Blinded Adults [4(o)4], are listed in Section 4 and discussed in Chapter 4. *The Elders Project* [1B(o)1] was concerned with the general skills and training needs of visually impaired elderly people and has also been discussed elsewhere in this book.

The RCEVH's important longitudinal investigation of cognitive development and school achievement in visually impaired pupils began in 1973 and was continuing at the time of our review. The overall study is not listed in the Directory, but three papers emanating from it are noted there (see index of Contents) and are relevant to the present discussion (Tobin, 1987; Tobin and Hill, 1988, 1989). These papers report the attitudes and values of visually impaired teenagers on the threshold of adulthood, illustrating the dilemmas for policy and practice in seeking to promote independence and normality through the provision of services to meet special needs. The majority of the young people interviewed either had a congenital visual impairment or had acquired significant sight loss within the first twelve months of life.

Tobin (1987) discusses teenagers' views on special and mainstream schooling. The interviewees had all begun their educational careers when the dominant philosophical emphasis of policy and practice was towards special school provision, whereas current educational policy favours integrating disabled children into mainstream schooling wherever possible. The majority of interviewees had attended special schools. Although sixty-seven per cent thought that this was better for them than integration into mainstream schooling, their responses reflected an awareness of the social and educational advantages and disadvantages of both approaches.

Tobin and Hill (1988) consider the career, marriage and leisure aspirations of the sample, indicating that these reflected a range of interests which cannot readily be seen as specific to visually impaired teenagers. However, in their discussions of the topics the interviewees showed a realistic recognition of the limits which their impairment placed on their aspirations and fantasies.

Tobin and Hill (1989) examine the concerns expressed by visually impaired teenagers about the present and the future. The young people in the RCEVH sample appeared to have similar concerns about worldwide problems such as nuclear war as their peers, as revealed by surveys of sighted teenagers.

Tobin and Hill's respondents did not look to medical science to 'cure' their own sight problems, but were concerned not to pass them on to any children they themselves might have. They felt that medical research should focus on finding cures for cancer. The young people interviewed also discussed the hostile and stigmatizing attitudes which their impairment aroused in some sighted people, offering the researchers examples of their experiences. The teenagers made suggestions for overcoming some of these problems of prejudice or ignorance. None of the other studies which we identified dealt explicitly with the issue of prejudice as experienced by visually impaired people, although Shore (1985) [1A(c)3] noted an ageist attitude in many social services departments.

The small study by the Chester Blind Welfare Society, *Comparison of Education Facilities for Visually Impaired Youngsters in Clwyd and Cheshire* [7(c)1], also addressed the issue of special 'versus' integrated education. The project reported by the Royal London Society for the Blind, *Further Education Needs, Academic and Social, of the Blind and Partially Sighted* [7(o)1], was concerned with the problems experienced in the community by ex-pupils of a special school.

Employment

The employment of people with significant sight loss is an extensive and specialized field. Employment is of course an important aspect of life for many visually impaired people below retirement age, and a concern of young people still at school or in further education. Research and development in the areas of education and training, rehabilitation, enhancement of low vision etc., many of them involving the use of information and other forms of modern technology, are markedly increasing the employability of people with sight problems. However, this is another field which could be seen as not being central to our immediate concerns. In the context of our review, research relevant to the employment of visually impaired people was treated in a similar manner to research concerning their education. Some projects were reported to us and included, but, as with education, the extent of coverage is uncertain.

The RNIB has led the field in the examination of employment experiences and opportunities relevant to visually impaired people. Some recent work from this source was included in our review; for example joint projects with a branch of the then Training Agency, which at the time was part of the Employment Department Group.[1] Neither local authorities nor academic institutions appeared to be directly involved in research on employment issues - although much of RCEVH's work concerning new technology (Directory: Section 4) appeared to have potential applications in an employment context, whilst one of the BMRU's listed studies [4(c)1] concerned assessment procedures at the RNIB's Rehabilitation Centre at Torquay, which has a key national role and relevance.

Lomas had carried out extensive and detailed work for the RNIB. His reports (1986a, 1986b, 1986c) drew on Census data, material from the ESRC Data Archive, from the then Manpower Services Commission, and from studies undertaken for the RNIB by Shankland Cox Partnerships (1985a, 1985b) and Moss (1985). Lomas consulted with central government departments, professional interest groups, training institutions, voluntary co-ordinating bodies, and staff in all sections of the RNIB concerned with employment opportunities for visually impaired people. As with other major RNIB research commissions during this period, the primary objective was to clarify the Institute's own current and future role.

The three reports by Lomas referred to in the previous paragraph are not listed in the Directory; discussion here concentrates on the more accessible *A Sense of Purpose: A Study of Visually Handicapped People and their Search for Work* [8(c)3], prepared by the RNIB's Employment Development Group and published in the same year (RNIB, 1986).

The findings of *A Sense of Purpose* were remarkably consistent with those of other studies identified in our review which did not directly address employment issues, for example Collins' study for the Partially Sighted Society [1B(c)1] and the Shore Report (Shore, 1985) [1A(c)3]. Both Collins and Shore found that social services departments had difficulty in maintaining accurate registers of blind and partially sighted people; in *A Sense of Purpose*, employment registers of visually impaired people were found to suffer similar limitations. Members of the sample of people with sight problems interviewed expressed a need for a better standard of counselling, as did clients in Collins' and Shore's studies. Counselling was also identified as a training need by the NFER in *Beyond Vision* (Maychell and Smart, 1990) [4(c)7], and as an important aspect of good practice by the SSI in *A Wider Vision* (1988b).

The BMRU's work on the psycho-social dimensions of mobility training (Directory: Sections 2, 3 and 4) is relevant to a consideration of the psycho-social benefits of obtaining work - the 'sense of purpose' referred to in the title of the RNIB study. The authors of the latter also suggested that other important influences on the ability of visually impaired people to take up employment include their general levels of health and the standards of education and training they have attained. Similarly, Dodds, Gaskell and Hellawell (1989) argue that clients' perceived social support and general health should be included in a specialist assessment, for example when considering a client's response to an offer of training. *Beyond Vision* also identified the issue of motivation, the various dimensions of which have been conceptually 'unpacked' by the BMRU (BMRU, 1989; Dodds, 1988; 1989), as needing greater attention in the training context.

RNIB had been working with the Psychological Services Branch of the then Training Agency[2] [8(c)1], [8(c)2] to pilot and evaluate new ways of providing an advisory service to visually impaired people. The role of the Blind Persons Resettlement Officer had been abolished under this scheme, which had direct involvement from the RNIB's Employment Advisory Service in the form of a training and advisory service to Disablement Resettlement Officers. A limited evaluation of the new service by clients and staff had been repeated over time, using 'a standards based approach'. This involved saying in advance what levels of performance would be expected of a good service and then checking how far the service had met them. The standard chosen was seventy per cent of the respondents to a survey saying that for them the service was operating 'satisfactorily' or 'more than satisfactorily'. Conversely, if more than thirty per cent expressed dissatisfaction it could be concluded that a problem needing further investigation had been identified.

Overall satisfaction with the different aspects of the pilot service varied over time and between clients and staff, but most staff and a majority of clients were reported as thinking that 'the pilot arrangements [were] working satisfactorily'. However, 'the standards [had] not been met in some aspects'. The two most important areas identified for improvement were staff training and resources.

The report on the first six months of the project [8(c)1] suggested that clients' satisfaction with the service rested on 'how the service [was] being delivered rather than what [was] delivered' [emphases in original]. However, McCallum, its author, cautioned that in judging standards the content as well as the style of service delivery should be taken into account. It is interesting to relate this finding to the BMRU's work on teaching styles in the training agencies [4(c)1], [4(c)3], [4(c)6], which indicated over-attention to the content of mobility training and insufficient awareness of the effect of the style of the instructor or teacher.

The Training Agency studies also further demonstrated, in the specific field concerned, the difficulties involved in identifying and maintaining accurate registers of visually impaired people who might benefit from particular services. These issues have already been noted both in connection with general information on the numbers and needs of visually impaired - and for that matter otherwise disabled - people, and in the context of other specific areas of provision such as that for groups of people with special needs.

The RNIB also reported two ongoing research projects on the employment needs of visually impaired people. One involved a pair of parallel *Employment Rehabilitation Feasibility Studies*, one covering England, Wales and Northern Ireland, the other Scotland [8(o)1]. The second project was *Vocational Opportunities for the Visually Impaired with Manual and Allied Skills* [8(o)2].

Notes

1   Further changes within the Employment Department Group during 1990 led to the Training Agency (previously the Training Commission and prior to that the Manpower Services Commission) being disbanded. Its main functions are now located within the Training Enterprise and Education Directorate (TEED).

2   See note 1.

6 Joint research projects

Introduction

Given the nature of visual impairment and the responses to it which were the focus of our review, and given also the current policy context, we were particularly interested in evidence of collaborative working between and amongst social services departments, health authorities and voluntary bodies. As applied researchers, we were also interested in the actual and potential contributions of academically based or independent research centres to policy and practice development. A number of the projects reported were examples of various forms of collaboration. This has been noted in passing in the preceding chapters, but the importance of this theme merits treatment in a separate short chapter.

It is necessary to make quite explicit here the distinctions between and amongst: (i) collaborative planning; (ii) joint work in the context of service development and/or service delivery initiatives; and (iii) joint research activity. The third of these may, but equally well may not, form part of or critically reflect upon and examine the first two. We found only a relatively small number of studies of joint social care initiatives, particularly evaluative studies of such developments, but this is not of itself evidence of an overall lack of joint working at policy and practice levels in this field. It does, however, give some grounds for supposing that there was in fact such a shortfall.

The criteria for inclusion in the Directory mean that the projects listed are *research* projects as defined in Chapter 2. The types of collaboration identified in the present chapter are therefore essentially various forms of joint working in an applied research context. Different kinds of financial collaboration were most prominent; indeed we specifically asked respondents for information on the funding of projects. Although the nature and level of funding was not clear in all cases, a number of overlapping models were indicated (see below).

It may be significant that of the projects included in the Directory which apparently involved some degree of collaboration, a substantial proportion were either general surveys of service organization and strategy or of client need, including two conducted in a 'joint planning' context. The other most prominent grouping was of studies concerning a sub-group with special needs within the total client group; here again the studies concerned were generally of a needs survey type. The small number of evaluated service initiatives reported overall each involved a collaborative element, both in the development itself and in the evaluation. In some instances therefore, joint provision or shared access to information was evident.

It has of course long been common in the field of visual impairment for a local authority to appoint a local voluntary organization as its agent in respect of providing particular services or administering registration procedures. Current policy imperatives seem likely to encourage this practice to become more widespread and for it to be extended to other client groups.

Most of the research projects identified and capable of being designated as 'joint', involved social services department/voluntary agency collaboration, with some examples of health service/voluntary sector partnership. The involvement of both local health and social services authorities in a research context concerning services for people with a visual impairment was, to judge from our findings at least, surprisingly rare, although a small number of examples were identified.

The collaborative activities of three voluntary organizations, as evidenced in our review, merit special mention. The bodies concerned are the RNIB, the Bristol Royal Society for the Blind, and the Partially Sighted Society. Before and during the period under review, the RNIB had been a significant sponsor of studies and projects undertaken by local authorities, by academic institutions, and by other, often local, voluntary organizations; it also supported educational and medical research. Bristol Royal Society for the Blind had been active in supporting research across agency boundaries and over a wide range of subjects. The Partially Sighted Society also supported research across agency boundaries, mainly to improve services for visually impaired people with residual vision.

The various forms of collaboration evidenced by the projects reported to us are set out and exemplified below. For the reasons already outlined, the most common forms of collaboration indicated were where two or more organizations got together to conduct or commission a study, resourced jointly from their own funds or from elsewhere, or where financial support by one or more bodies enabled another to undertake research. In the latter case, the question of access - for example on the part of a voluntary body or an independent research centre to local or health authority records and/or service users - represented another form of collaboration. A certain amount of indirect information about examples of direct joint working was implicit in some of the brief accounts given by respondents.

In the Directory only one entry appears for each project. Any direct joint involvement in individual projects (i.e. excluding purely involvement as a funding body) is indicated wherever possible. As pointed out in Chapter 2, equivalent notifications of projects which appeared to be joint activities involving two (or more) potential respondents were not always received from all parties.

Forms of collaboration

1. Two or more agencies working together in the context of seeking information, based on research, for planning or strategic development purposes. Examples were the work of the RNIB, RNID, National Deaf-Blind League and SENSE (as, collectively, the Deaf-Blind Services Liaison Group) which led to *Breaking Through* [5(c)1]; Bedfordshire Joint Care Planning Team's ten-year *Strategic Framework* [1A(o)3]; and the work of the South Devon Review and Planning Group [1A(c)6]. The Partially Sighted Society was substantially involved in the last-mentioned context, and also worked closely with a number of local and health authorities in the South West [1B(c)1], including Avon Social Services Department, with whom the Bristol Royal Society for the Blind had also collaborated closely on a number of projects, e.g. [2(o)1] and [1A(c)4].

2. The development work which was being done by the RNIB Consultancy Service with Oldham, Tameside [1A(c)7] and Lancashire Social Services Departments, and with Oldham Health Authority.

3. An example of a joint service initiative which had also been evaluated was *Operation Cataract* [1C(c)1]. This was funded by Worthing Health Authority and the Impact Foundation. A local hotel had also been closely involved in the project, as had the Red Cross, WRVS and Rotary Club. This exemplified both direct and indirect financial contributions from voluntary organizations; the indirect resources in this case taking the form of clerical, transport and other support services which would otherwise have been provided by employees of statutory agencies.

4. One agency appointing another as its agent. An example was the Department of Social Services and Housing of the London Borough of

Bromley having appointed the Kent Association for the Blind to act as its agent to assess the needs of local visually impaired people [1B(o)4]. Another was Devon Social Services Department's commissioning of SENSE South West to survey the needs of deaf-blind people in its area [5(o)3].

5. The core funding of a specialist research unit in the field of visual impairment. The key example was the Department of Health's support for the ongoing research programme of the Blind Mobility Research Unit at the University of Nottingham.

6. Commissioning a major study, usually from an academic or independent research body: e.g. the then DHSS commissioning the National Foundation for Educational Research to study the main training courses for specialist workers [4(c)7].

7. A charity or voluntary organization funding research carried out by another charity or voluntary organization. For example, the Cecilia Trust was funding the survey of needs being carried out by Chester Blind Welfare Society [1B(o)6].

8. Bursary schemes. *Day Care for Visually Impaired People with Learning Difficulties* [6(c)1], and *Visual Assessment at the Wyvern SEC, Pewsey* [6(c)4] were both funded by Bristol Royal Society for the Blind under such a scheme. The bursary holders' own employing agency/ies also bore some of the costs of these studies.

9. Financial support for a specific study from a combination of sources, often a mixture of national and local, statutory and voluntary bodies. Examples reported included:

Bristol Royal Society for the Blind's study of *Mobility Aids for Visually Impaired People* [3(o)1] was being funded in part via the Society's bursary scheme (see above), with additional funding from the Guide Dogs for the Blind Association and other sources.

The RNIB, the Department of Health, and Opportunities for Volunteers had combined to support the survey of needs being undertaken by Cambridgeshire Society for the Blind and Partially Sighted [1B(o)5] and the evaluation of the provision of an adviser/counsellor at an eye hospital, being undertaken by Brighton Society for the Blind [1C(o)1].

The Department of Health, South East Thames Regional Health Authority, and a private charity acting as guarantor for any eventual overspend, were funding the SRAB's project on *Services for Multi-Handicapped Visually Impaired People* [6(o)1].

The then Manpower Services Commission and Hampshire Social Services Department shared the costs of the survey of the needs of visually impaired people in Hampshire, undertaken by Hampshire Association for the Care of the Blind [1B(c)3].

RNIB, Birmingham Royal Institution for the Blind, various charities, and Birmingham University, had jointly funded a variety of research projects carried out by the University's Research Centre for the Education of the Visually Handicapped.

An external source of funding for the Partially Sighted Society's *Evaluation of a Low Vision Training Programme* [4(o)2] was reported but not named, and an un-named private sponsor was funding the Royal London Society for the Blind's study of *Further Educational Needs, Academic and Social, of the Blind and Partially Sighted* [7(o)1].

Part III
FUTURE RESEARCH
PRIORITIES

7 A framework for future research

Introduction

The studies identified in the course of our review, listed in the Directory (Appendix), and discussed in Part II of this book, must be situated in the context of current policy and practice in order to identify priority areas for future research: the aim of our original review, carried forward to this book. In our report on the review (Lovelock and Edge, 1991), we sought to do this with reference to the key themes of the White Paper *Caring for People* (DoH, 1989a), identifying how these themes related specifically to identifying and meeting the social support needs of visually impaired people. *Caring for People* appeared as our study commenced. The NHS and Community Care Act 1990 which followed it was enacted only after our report was drafted and this legislation was of course not fully implemented until April 1993.

The 'agenda for change' presented in the 1989 White Paper, including the tensions between differing conceptions of choice and empowerment embedded in it (see Chapter 1), still seems the most appropriate backdrop to the broad brush proposals of this concluding chapter. This is so notwithstanding the greater precision perhaps now possible on the basis of a specific new legislative context, with additional detail supplied by the extensive guidance on implementing 'community care' which has issued from the Department of Health (e.g. DoH, 1990; DoH/Scottish Office, 1991). This understanding provides a rationale for presenting here in essentially its original form the discussion of the overall body of work collated during our review and, based upon this, the identification of an agenda for future research. Rather than seeking to update this discussion as such, which would in effect have necessitated a 'repeat' of the whole review exercise, a brief overview of subsequent developments is offered in a Postscript.

Before reminding readers of the key themes of *Caring for People*, or, put another way, of the main dimensions of 'the community care agenda', some observations on the overall body of research collated provide an additional element of background to the discussion.

The body of recent research identified and reviewed

If 'research' is understood in terms of systematic and rigorous studies of a closely defined subject matter, then most of the relevant work falling within the criteria of our review had been or was being done in two major academically based centres: the Blind Mobility Research Unit, based in the Department of Psychology at the University of Nottingham (much of whose work has been funded by the Department of Health on a rolling contract), and the Research Centre for the Education of the Visually Handicapped, based in the School of Education at the University of Birmingham. To this should be added the important study of the specialist training courses, conducted for the Department of Health by the National Foundation for Educational Research. However, only a sprinkling of other academic work was identified as coming within the parameters of our review.

Several substantial studies carried out or commissioned and published by the Royal National Institute for the Blind, and included in the Directory, were more directly related to policy than was most of the work based in the specialist research centres. However, and notwithstanding the general significance of the RNIB's research, particularly in fields such as employment, the work included essentially related to the Institute's own policy and practice development initiatives.

Valuable studies, with a wider relevance than simply that to their own immediate local contexts, were reported by smaller voluntary bodies, such as the Partially Sighted Society and the Bristol Royal Society for the Blind.

A substantial number of projects were brought to our attention by other local agencies, both statutory and voluntary. However, the overall research contribution represented by these must be summarized as rather piecemeal and for the most part parochial, however appropriate such a local focus may be in the particular context of each of the bodies concerned. This body of work also had a tendency either to be highly specific or to be superficially general, without being in either case technically very rigorous. Indeed, much that has been included in the Directory might be discarded by some as scarcely research at all. We ourselves excluded a good deal of material about development initiatives, together with a substantial number of publications which, whilst of relevance, appeared to lack a basis in anything which could justifiably be termed research.

There were noticeable differences of style and focus between the two main bodies of work characterized in the preceding paragraphs. Most of the more formal or academic research reviewed had given little attention to the overall planning and organization of services. Much of the more operational work, typically carried out in a local authority or small voluntary agency context, had tended largely to take existing definitions of need and approaches to meeting it as given.

Many of the studies reported by local authority social services departments or small voluntary organizations were essentially numerical assessments of aggregate local needs. Unfortunately, differences in definition and sampling basis make comparison or overall aggregation between these numerous studies extremely difficult.

The RNIB's *General Needs Survey* (Bruce et al., 1991; Walker et al., 1992) [1B(o)2], current at the time of the review, sought a national picture in essentially quantitative terms. Prior to this project, with its representative sample, and apart from small-scale local work, mainly in the voluntary sector, little direct and/or systematic attention had been paid to care and support needs as felt by people with sight problems themselves, nor to their experience of services. We found no studies giving focal attention to the needs of relatives and others supporting visually impaired people.

Our review was able to identify little substantial collaborative research: in particular, few examples involving both the main statutory services at the heart of social care. This gap is noteworthy, especially in the crucial area of referral, assessment, and the provision of rehabilitative services and continuing support.

In carrying out our review, we were struck, as relative 'outsiders', by the 'small world' feel of the inter-relations between the few specialist academic centres involved and the major voluntary agencies, with everyone seemingly knowing everybody else. Conversely, individual local or health authorities, and small voluntary organizations, did not seem to be part of this circle, and whilst we may not have recognized the full extent of specific collaboration taking place, there did seem to be a degree of unease on the part of 'the insiders' with regard to the wider world of practice in statutory and voluntary sector settings.

For example, when we visited the BMRU, staff implicitly referred to an 'implementation gap', between their research, the specialist training programmes which might be drawing directly upon it, and 'the front line' where rehabilitation work with individual visually impaired people takes place. Similarly, colleagues at the RCEVH indicated a keen awareness that despite their wish to contribute to improving practice they found it difficult to do so.

These feelings may connect with the NFER's conclusion, in its review of the specialist training courses, that too great an emphasis was being placed on how to teach the underlying skills to the officers in training, at the expense of how to teach the skills to the ultimate clientele. The problems concerning both the role and the supervision of specialist workers catering to a relatively small client group within a large generic social services department were recognized by the main research groups, but need to be addressed more directly. In this context it is notable that no local authorities reported being directly involved in research in the training field, nor were they prominent in most of the more specialized areas into which the projects we identified have been grouped.

In seeking a way forward with direct reference to 'community care' as generally understood, some of these impressions may help inform our thinking.

Caring for People and social care provision for visually impaired people

The following brief quotations from the White Paper *Caring for People* (DoH, 1989a, p. 9) indicate something of its overall thrust:

> Enabling people to live as independently as possible in the community is at the heart of community care. To do so, people frequently need both social care and health care ...

> ... Community care means providing the right level of intervention and support to enable people to achieve maximum independence and control over their own lives. For this aim to become a reality, the development of a wide range of services provided in a variety of settings is essential.

If these and similar commitments are taken as remaining central to national policy, research relevant to identifying and meeting the social support needs of visually impaired people, as of other groups, must *inter alia* pay attention to:

- the identification and review of overall need, as the basis for (local) planning

- monitoring and review of resources and overall provision (including the organization and management of services), as an integral part of service development

- provision of flexible services, targeted at individuals' assessed and reviewed needs, (perhaps adopting a care management approach), including services for members of groups with special needs

- consumer sensitivity and choice, in terms of the availability of information and advice and suitable complaints procedures, and user

74

involvement in both individual and overall care planning and delivery

- collaboration at planning, operational management and front-line delivery levels between a number of statutory and independent sector agencies, within an increasingly mixed economy of care

- the needs of carers

- the training and staff development needs generated by the foregoing imperatives.

A number of official documents concerning services for people with physical or sensory impairments, for example *Care in Action* (DHSS, 1981), the *Health Services Resource Assumptions and Planning Guidelines* set out in HC(88)43, and the Health Notice/Local Authority Social Services Letter HN(88)26, HN(FP)(88)25, LASSL(88)8, predated *Caring for People* and pre-figured some of its general emphases. They also stressed prevention and active rehabilitation as priorities, noted the special needs of and the poor provision hitherto for people with multiple impairments (for example people with dual sensory loss or with physical and/or sensory impairments in addition to severe learning difficulties). Further, they drew attention to the common needs of disabled people in general, and to the needs of carers (e.g. for respite), and noted that such needs change over time.

The recommendations concerning the nature and organization of services for visually impaired people contained in a number of specific reports, are strikingly similar to the general themes of *Caring for People* and more recent guidance on implementing the community care legislation (e.g. DoH, 1990; DoH/Scottish Office, 1991). The attention of those responsible for local service provision was drawn in a series of documents, including *A Wider Vision* (SSI, 1988b) and *Co-ordinating Services for Visually Handicapped People* (DoH, 1989b), to the importance of effective referral and assessment systems, of adequate rehabilitation and continuing care services, and perhaps above all to the need for co-ordination and collaboration between the several agencies necessarily involved in providing services. The specific references to children with disabilities in the 1989 Children Act are also relevant in this connection. *Out of Isolation* (Best et al., 1987) [6(c)3], *Breaking Through* (RNIB (Deaf-Blind Services Liaison Group), 1988) [5(c)1], and *Sign Posts* (SSI, 1989) also each paid particular attention to these and other aspects of supporting people with special needs.

The broad direction of Government policy indicated in *Caring for People* and in the parallel White Papers on Primary Health Care (DHSS, 1987b) and on the NHS (DoH, 1989c), and embodied in subsequent legislation, also stresses and seeks to combine the efficient use of resources with the provision of high quality services aimed at meeting individual need, the reduction of dependence on services, especially those offered by the statutory sector, and the enhancement of individual choice. In the field of visual impairment, as elsewhere, the stated overall policy aim is to enable a worthwhile quality of life through rehabilitation and continuing care, preferably 'in the community'.

The tensions embedded in these aims, in particular those between identifying need and providing high quality services on the one hand, and reducing dependence on the public purse on the other, are set in high relief by the findings (methodological and political critiques notwithstanding (see Preface)) of the OPCS *Surveys of Disability in Great Britain* (1988 and 1989) and the RNIB's *General Needs Survey* (Bruce et al., 1991; Walker et al., 1992) [1B(o)2]. These have powerfully underlined the fact that people over retirement age dominate amongst those with sight problems, including amongst those with the severest impairments. The majority, however, are partially sighted rather than totally blind. They also commonly have a range of other disabilities, which may be amenable to ameliorative intervention and support from service providing agencies.

Our review of research set out from two hypotheses. The first was the Department of Health's sense that recent and current research in the area of social care/services for visually impaired people, including research which it had itself funded, had, whilst important and valuable, perhaps been rather narrow in relation to the actual profile of the overall client group and the needs of its members. The second was our own suspicion that, given the way in which the relevant services are organized and delivered, valuable research - perhaps of a less academic nature, but nevertheless worthy of acknowledgement and attention - might have been done or be ongoing within local statutory agencies and national and local voluntary organizations.

Generally speaking, both views were confirmed, although within an overall low level of research activity in absolute terms when compared with that concerning policy and care practice in respect of other client groups.

The projects identified, and the presentation and discussion in Part II of the body of relevant research as a whole, cast some light on the national policy themes identified above. These will now be discussed further under the following headings:

Identification of the population of visually impaired people: overall need and planning

Monitoring and review of existing provision and resources

Referral, assessment and review: identifying and meeting individual need

Taking account of service users' views

Inter-agency collaboration

Services for people with multiple impairments and special needs

The needs of carers

Staff development and training issues: specialist training; integration into mainstream provision; identification and dissemination of good practice.

A number of recommendations for further research are made in the course of the discussion which follows. As indicated in the Introduction to this chapter, the argument remains in essentially the form in which it was presented to the Department of Health in 1991. The Postscript offers an update, but it is the argument of this book as a whole that little has changed in the intervening years; at least, not so substantially as to render the proposals presented in the following pages redundant.

Identification of the population of visually impaired people: overall need and planning

In Part II, attention was drawn to the changing demographic context of need, to the difficulties of definition, and to the inappropriateness of basing estimates on registration data. These points are not discussed in detail again here.

The practical difficulty of accurately identifying the size and breakdown of the population of people with a visual impairment has been a persistent theme in numerous recent reports produced by the Department of Health, including the SSI, and by the major national voluntary bodies in the field. Visually impaired people with an additional hearing impairment, or with severe learning difficulties, appear to have been particularly difficult subgroups to identify. One aspect of this has been that the process of 'classification by labelling' which commonly takes place within agencies planning and providing services, often in terms of broad client groups or services (already) received, has tended to focus on one set of needs and to mask others.

The returns and reports received from social services departments and voluntary organizations in the course of our review confirmed that these issues were beginning to be acknowledged in a number of localities. However, the number of 'nil returns' received must also be borne in mind, perhaps especially those from local authorities. Certainly there was further confirmation from the studies notified to us that many of the relevant statutory and voluntary agencies did not hold accurate information on the numbers and needs of people in their areas with various forms and degrees of visual impairment.

Statutory agencies not only need to know the extent and nature of need in their area; they have a duty to know under existing legislation.[1] In this context there was some evidence from the studies reported to us, particularly the reviews and surveys listed in Section 1 of the Directory, to suggest that more widespread collaboration between the several relevant local statutory and voluntary agencies in the collection and sharing of information would be a step forward. The agencies involved in providing services for visually impaired people need to examine the problems and practices which inhibit the sharing of information. The inevitably partial picture of need provided by aggregating numbers and categories of known clients could at least then be made more comprehensive than at present.

A number of social services departments were or had been carrying out local reviews and surveys, but these were commonly based on known clients and existing services. Different definitions and sample bases in such studies make aggregation on a regional or national basis unreliable. On balance the voluntary sector seemed more likely to have approached the issue of assessing aggregate need from the perspective of potential clients in the wider population. No doubt the different frames of reference are influenced respectively by the fact that the voluntary organizations operate as pressure groups, in which context reference to larger numbers of potential clients may be more persuasive, whilst local authorities have at best an understandable ambivalence to uncovering unmet need.

Certainly quantitative and qualitative information about need should be brought together; much of the work referred to has tended to emphasize one or the other. The RNIB's *General Needs Survey* (Bruce et al., 1991; Walker et al., 1992) [1B(o)2], building upon the *OPCS Surveys of Disability in Great Britain* (1988 and 1989), has advanced the information base for national and local planning.[2] The RNIB study could be built upon to define a typology of groups and identify their needs in broad terms. To obtain large enough samples it may make sense to explore this in a European context, which might anyway be appropriate for more general reasons in the longer term. Local planning guidance could flow from this work, as well as national policy implications.

Monitoring and review of existing provision and resources

Ongoing review of policy, organization and practice is increasingly recognized as an integral part of service development. The requirements of the NHS and Community Care Act 1990 that local authorities publish Community Care Plans, make available specific information on resources and services, attend to 'quality assurance', and seek to stimulate a 'mixed economy of care', with the consequent development of a 'contract culture', all point to the increasing importance of this orientation and encourage the increased explicitness required. However, it will not be easy to achieve even and high standards across the range of care services needed by visually impaired people. Such uniform quality may prove even more difficult to achieve in the context of an increasing number of independent providers than it has hitherto been with 'merely' (several) statutory sector

78

agencies involved.[3]

As regards local authority social services departments, our review suggested a marked lack of standardization between - and even within - individual authorities. The SSI's investigations, reported in *A Wider Vision* (1988b), revealed many social services departments unable to produce written strategies or plans for the development of their services for visually impaired people, registers out of date, and inadequate client records. Some of the information collected from social services departments in the course of our own research indicated attempts to respond positively to the recommendations of *A Wider Vision* and other national reports. However, our review also added to the widespread sense that resources and services relevant to people with visual impairments remained inadequate - particularly in the field of social rehabilitation - fragmented, unco-ordinated, and difficult to access.

Caring for People (DoH, 1989a) and other contemporary official reports suggested an increasingly prominent role for the voluntary sector. However, the RNIB study *Working Together* [1A(c)8], which examined 'the scope for improving links between the RNIB and local societies', drew attention to the enormous variation among organizations which can be classified as 'voluntary' and are for or of people with sight problems. The RNIB is demonstrating its potential in a number of ways: by developing services, both direct and advisory, at a regional level, including for groups with special needs, and by offering consultancy services to local statutory and voluntary agencies. In so far as local voluntary organizations have the capacity to play a larger role as agents of 'enabling' local authorities and/or as partners in joint provision, they need to become more self-conscious about their aims and objectives and to accept a similar level of public scrutiny to that of local authorities, at the expense of some of their rightly cherished independence and autonomy. The potential costs of this evolution must not be ignored.

Thus, if exhortations to local authorities, health authorities and the voluntary sector to combine to promote and develop their services - for visually impaired people and for other groups - are to bear fruit, there must be sound, realistic, and sensitive guidance on how this might be done, and encouragement for local initiatives. Joint reviews of existing provision, with careful attention to the health/social care interface, may be part of the way forward and should be encouraged. A small number of projects which could be said to represent modest examples of this were reported to us.

There is a need for a national research based review of the nature and level of social services departments' provision to meet the needs of visually impaired people, including stated policies and how departments are organized and managed for this purpose. This could follow the lines recommended in *A Wider Vision* (SSI, 1988b). It should include an examination of how these services - in effect how staff at various levels - inter-relate with

79

others, particularly in the health service and the voluntary sector. Social services departments' plans for change in the light of broader 'community care' developments should be incorporated.

Referral, assessment and review: identifying and meeting individual need

The process of certification and referral is of long-standing concern in the field of services for people with sight problems. More generally, some of the most important general themes of *Caring for People* (DoH, 1989a) centred around assessment and care management. It is important to distinguish conceptually between the following: certification as the statement (on Form BD8) on the basis of medical examination that a person's degree of visual impairment is sufficient that they are eligible for registration as blind or partially sighted; their onward referral (via Form BD8) to a social services department; their possible registration (with its bearing upon receipt of certain benefits); and the assessment of their social care needs, and possible subsequent service provision.

A number of the studies identified in our review added to and confirmed the picture presented in *A Wider Vision* (SSI, 1988b). Time lags between ophthalmic examination and the receipt of a BD8 form by the relevant local authority were common. Social services departments varied in their response to receipt of BD8s, with further delays occurring at the various subsequent stages of the process. Some social services departments automatically registered clients, without consulting them; others used the referral for (possible) registration as a means of initiating an assessment process with clients if they so desired. The information supplied on the BD8 was seen as being of limited and varying usefulness in the context of a social care assessment.[4]

The content of the BD8 and the processes surrounding its use have been sources of concern for some time. A revised version of the form was introduced in April 1990, and the Report to the Minister for the Disabled on *Co-ordinating Services for Visually Handicapped People* (DoH, 1989b) suggested that the SSI conduct a study on the impact of the report's recommendations and the changes in the content and use of the new BD8 form.[5] Such a study could be an invaluable contribution to analysing the point of entry to rehabilitation services and the response of those services to their potential users. It is imperative that such a study takes a broad rather than a narrow perspective on the BD8 process and that it is of sufficient scale in terms of the sample of areas involved. Both health and social services 'sides' of the process must be examined.

Turning from referral to assessment, *Caring for People* (DoH, 1989a) included in its six key objectives for service delivery across all client groups:

... to make proper assessment of need and good case management the cornerstone of high quality care. Packages of care should then be designed in line with individual needs and preferences. (p. 5)[6]

The White Paper later stated:

The Government proposes that the responsibility for ensuring that an assessment is made should be a specific duty of the local authority. This does not mean that other agencies should be excluded, nor that local authorities can or should make decisions on services managed by other agencies. A single individual should be responsible for dealing with each case effectively. (p. 19)

The White Paper was followed by the NHS and Community Care Act 1990, then by a series of announced delays in implementing key elements of the legislation, including the specific provisions regarding assessment and care management. Several issues in this area, none of them new, provoked heated debate amongst social workers, their managers, and social work educators. Prominent were: the extent to which the approach recommended was in fact already common (or at least 'best possible') professional practice; how to establish which potential clients require a 'full' initial assessment; when and to what extent multidisciplinary assessment is necessary, and how this may be effectively and efficiently carried out.

SSI studies and other reports from the Department of Health referred to extensively in these pages indicated that assessment skills and procedures have long been among the weakest features of local authority social services departments' provision for visually impaired people. Associated and commonly voiced criticisms have included that many social services departments lack sufficient numbers of staff properly trained in the assessment of the broad needs of people with sight problems, and that they fail to provide appropriate services to meet them. Several studies included in our review indicated the central place of assessment skills in the appropriate training of specialist workers and the considerable scope for further development in this respect in the context of current training programmes.

The need to draw to some degree on the expertise of other agencies in the context of assessment, especially the contribution of various health service staff, and then to make available an appropriate combination of social, health and voluntary sector services, is common in relation to many clients. This certainly applies in many cases of visual impairment, where a range of services provided by different agencies is commonly required, not all of them specifically related to sight problems.

Initial assessment represents an early stage of work with a person, whether with sight problems or other needs. In the care management approach, with which the White Paper and subsequent guidance and discussion links assessment, the latter is preceded by 'case finding'/referral and followed by designing and 'packaging' services to meet assessed needs, then by subsequent monitoring and review.

Without regular and adequate review in individual cases, changing needs can go unrecognized and unmet. Such changes may be due to improvements as well as reductions in ability. Well-known studies of the home help service, meals on wheels and the provision of various daily living aids (see Goldberg and Connelly (1982) for a review), have shown that not only do recipients' real wants and needs go unmet due to standard responses being made by agencies on the basis of inadequate assessment, but also that needs change so that provision made becomes unnecessary, inappropriate or inadequate. The studies identified in our review indicated similar mismatches in the field of present concern, although no specific attention was given to this issue.

The process of referral, assessment and review is a high priority area for research and development work, on a broader basis than review of the new BD8, although this latter task is important in itself. This key interface between health and social care requires examination from a number of perspectives, including those of different professional groups, of service users, and of carers. The process of registration, assessment, provision of services, and ongoing review is an extension of the initial ophthalmic assessment and certification of eligibility for registration as either blind or partially sighted, moving from an essentially medical context into the area of social services department and voluntary sector provision.

In this general context, research and practice must specifically acknowledge the significance of the rehabilitation and other needs of elderly people with visual impairments: both those needs related to their sight problems and their other service and care needs. Similarly, the assessment and provision of services for (other) multiply impaired groups must be kept in view.

Finally, in so far as these assessment tasks related to the provision of social support services must have a sound basis in measured capacities and limitations, there is a need to continue fundamental work such as that of the BMRU aimed at improving the reliability and validity of visual assessment procedures, especially in relation to the variety of conditions termed collectively here as 'low vision', which have been relatively neglected until recently.

Taking account of service users' views

Caring for People (DoH, 1989a) strongly advocated that users of services should be actively involved in various ways in the planning, provision[7] and monitoring of services, both at an individual and an aggregate level, in pursuit of both choice and quality. This represented official recognition

82

of a 'movement' building in the social care field for many years, not least amongst various groups of disabled people, whose felt needs and expectations have been changing. Whilst these issues must be addressed in the context of the planning, management, organization and face-to-face delivery of services, research and monitoring closely associated with the necessary changes has an important role to play.

Some of the projects listed in the Directory drew upon the views and experiences of people with sight problems. This was most evident in the context of attempting to (re)assess the kinds and categories of need and what mixes of services might be necessary to address them, and in appraising existing service provision. There are a number of areas where additional local consumer studies could contribute to the improvement of services for people with sight problems. There is also considerable scope for systematic and broadly based research on the views and experiences of visually impaired people. Some examples follow.

Visually impaired people's experiences of blindness or partial sight, and their *own* perceptions of their resultant individual needs, represent related and important areas for further study, to illuminate the possible mismatch of services and felt needs referred to in the previous sub-section. Also, users' accounts of their experiences of the process of certification, referral and initial assessment would be a vital component of a study in this key area; any review of the working of the new BD8 form should incorporate this dimension.

Further research on the experience of the trauma of sight loss or reduction could inform service development and lead to practical benefits for users. In particular, questions about the value of providing social and psychological support as well as ophthalmic diagnosis and assessment at the onset of visual impairment could usefully be explored through the views of those directly concerned, many of whom will be elderly and have other needs.

An important dimension of 'consumerism' concerns the availability and nature of information about possible support services. Health service professionals, including opticians, general practitioners, and ophthalmologists, may be the first to become aware of the development of a visual impairment in an individual case. Research could examine the information made available to users and to carers in the context of examinations by each of these experts. Information about non-medical services, including the statutory entitlements of visually impaired people, should be a particular focus. Issues may arise here which would need to be addressed in the context of the training of various health (and other) professionals. A related study could examine the information supplied to users and carers in the context of assessment by social services departments for help in relation to sight problems. Important specific issues about inter-agency working would be highlighted by such studies.

Inter-agency collaboration

Collaboration at policy, planning, operational management and front-line delivery levels, between statutory and independent sector agencies, was another general exhortation of *Caring for People* (DoH, 1989a). In the particular field of concern here it has also been a recurring theme of numerous reports from the Department of Health and the major voluntary agencies, in particular 'the Shore Report' (1985) [1A(c)3], *Co-ordinating Services for Visually Handicapped People* (DoH, 1989b) and *A Wider Vision* (SSI, 1988b). It is clear that changing the practices of the agencies concerned is no small task.

Our review identified some studies which gave evidence of pockets of collaborative activity of various sorts, or which in themselves represented attempts jointly to plan or review services or to develop new forms of provision. Some of the reported work of the Partially Sighted Society has particular relevance here. The Society was doing pioneering collaborative work in terms of both planning and service provision; it had also carried out a number of relatively small-scale studies capable of being built upon. The RNIB had been particularly active in reviewing and subsequently taking initiatives of various kinds in the area of collaboration between itself, local voluntary organizations, and/or statutory agencies. Chapter 6 specifically examined the various types of financial and other collaborative arrangements illustrated by the joint research projects identified in our review.

On balance, however, and notwithstanding the foregoing remarks, we found rather few recent or ongoing studies specifically examining areas of collaborative activity and/or work at inter-agency interfaces. In particular, there were very few joint health/social services research projects in the field of visual impairment. This may or may not have been a direct reflection of a low level of substantive collaborative effort; certainly it appeared that little such activity had attracted research attention.

Research, particularly if associated with development work or concentrating upon the identification, analysis and dissemination of models of good practice, can play an important role as a catalyst to joint work. However, this potential has been restricted thus far in the visual impairment field , including by the apparent lack of substantive activity.

Nevertheless, there are research contributions which could presently be made in areas which are potentially sites for collaboration: in service planning, provision[8] and development. Such studies could examine the extent to which joint work is actually taking place. A number of the proposals in earlier sub-sections touch on issues where collaborative arrangements are of considerable importance. For example, in suggesting that there is scope (further enhanced by on-going organizational changes - see notes 7 and 8) for national research into the way in which social services departments are organized in respect of provision for people with

84

sight problems, the importance of giving attention to procedures and practices concerning collaborative working was noted. This should encompass the wider field of collaboration between health and social services authorities concerning visual impairment, as well as the particular health/social care interface in terms of referral and assessment. Some more specific possibilities are outlined in the following paragraphs.

Attention has been drawn at various points to questions around the need for information to be shared between agencies, for example in the context of the processes of certification, referral, registration, assessment and review in individual cases, and concerning overall service policy, planning and review. Research could examine the extent and nature of such sharing of information in practice, and identify the difficulties which are experienced by the staff involved.

With reference to sharing information between agencies, of which the use of the BD8 form is a crucial example, questions of privacy must be acknowledged. The debate engendered around the revision of the BD8 highlights the tension which can exist between an individual's right to privacy, for example concerning medical matters, and the needs of perhaps more than one authority for sufficient information to plan and provide adequate and appropriate services (see note 4).

Post-operative or post-treatment practices constitute a vital element of the health/social care interface in relation to visual impairment, and one where specifically social research is needed. A key link between medical and social services can be made via a social work contribution at eye hospitals and outpatient clinics. This is particularly relevant to after-care following treatment, or at the onset of visual impairment. Two projects with a direct bearing on this are included in the Directory, whilst reports from others commented on the appropriateness of such a service.

There are of course wider issues here about the uncertain future of social work in health settings, some of them linked with questions of possible future contracting across the health/social care interface. A study of the extent to which local authorities currently offer a service to their local eye hospitals and eye clinics, and their future plans, and/or about the nature and extent of any other such services offered and by whom, would be valuable. It could form part of the wider study of social services departments' contributions to the support of visually impaired people suggested above. There are also links with the proposal for work exploring users' views of the experience of sight loss/reduction and the kinds of help people with sight loss feel they need.

Services for people with multiple impairments and special needs

Out of Isolation (Best et al., 1987) [6(c)3] and *Breaking Through* (RNIB (Deaf-Blind Services Liaison Group), 1988) [5(c)1] were concerned respectively with services for people with severe learning difficulties as well as a visual impairment, and for people with dual sensory loss. Together with the other studies identified during our review concerning the needs and circumstances of people with a visual impairment and additional disabilities and needs - 'the minority within a minority' - these important reports suggest that these groups and their carers are likely to have more severe needs and are less likely to be receiving appropriate help than are people who suffer solely from impaired vision. Agencies have apparently found great difficulty in designing coherent strategies and appropriate and cost-effective service arrangements to meet these needs.

Voluntary bodies, in particular the large national organizations, appear to have taken the initiative as regards research into the social care needs of these groups, and to have been the major providers of the relevant services, for example guide-helpers for people with dual sensory impairment. However, our review suggested that some local authorities were beginning to address the issues of identifying need and ensuring the provision of services. In particular, *Breaking Through* and *Sign Posts* (SSI, 1989) seemed directly to have stimulated a number of local authority surveys and the setting up of local 'Standing Forums', typically involving several statutory and voluntary organizations. This is a prime field for continuing collaboration between the sectors, with associated research and monitoring in relation to the information and service development tasks involved.

People with low vision are not conventionally regarded as a special needs group in the sense used in this discussion; they are also specifically not in a minority position amongst those with sight problems. It should be recorded here, however, that continuing research is needed concerning low vision and the development of assessment techniques and services specifically designed to identify and maximize residual abilities.

The needs of carers

Caring for People (DoH, 1989a) directed statutory authorities, particularly social services departments, to pay much greater attention to the interests and contributions of carers in assessing the needs of potential direct users of services and in the provision of help. Carers were to be recognized as partners in designing and implementing 'packages of care'. Without carers' support many disabled people cannot live independently within the community. In this context, the direct needs of carers themselves were also to be acknowledged. The provision of information to carers of people with sight problems was mentioned earlier in discussing possible research drawing on users' views and experiences of the referral and assessment process. There are staff and service development issues here.

There is a notable gap in research into the particular concerns, experiences and needs of the informal carers of visually impaired people; certainly these topics were largely absent from the studies reported during our review. Indirect information was available from some of the studies listed on people with multiple impairments including sight loss, and there may have been a number of relevant studies in the education field, which we did not systematically survey. Parents were the main source of information on disabled children in the OPCS *Surveys of Disability in Great Britain* (Report 3 and Report 6, 1989).[9]

Research attention should be given to the specific roles and experiences of informal carers supporting visually impaired people. On each of the topics where a need for systematic studies to obtain the views of visually impaired people has already been identified, it is likely to be of interest to set carers' perspectives alongside them.

Staff development and training issues: specialist training; integration into mainstream provision; identification and dissemination of good practice

Service development inevitably involves staff development. As *Caring for People* (DoH, 1989a) acknowledged, training and development for front-line staff and managers at all levels is necessary to achieve and underpin the changes in practice enshrined in the new policies, in particular to identify, assess and meet need in a partnership between various service providers, users and carers. This is no less true in the field of visual impairment than elsewhere, and thus there is a training element relating to each of the foregoing parts of this discussion. In relation to this, the additional Training Support Programme specifically associated with the implementation of the community care legislation may be seen as adding to the pre-existing potential of the TSP initiative in respect of supporting elderly people, in particular for the in-service training of social services staff (*Social Services Training Support Programme: Financial Year 1990-91*, Local Authority Circular LAC(89)17). There are related training needs in respect of voluntary agency and health service workers, and therefore possibilities for joint training initiatives.

Specialist training

A central and long-standing theme in the field of provision for people with sight problems concerns the training of specialist workers to assist them (Beggs, 1985; SSI, 1988b). In turn, the organization and effectiveness of specialist training has also been a major focus of recent social research relevant to visual impairment. It featured prominently in our review, notably through *Beyond Vision* (Maychell and Smart, 1990), reporting the NFER's study for the Department of Health [4(c)7] of the courses offered by the NMC, NRAB and SRAB, and through some of the BMRU's work.

The Shore Report (1985) [1A(c)3] and the Partially Sighted Society's *The Client's View* [1B(c)1] were among other reported studies to cast light on specialist training issues. The main criticisms made in this body of work reflected many of the wider themes concerning the nature and needs of the client group: an over-concentration on mobility issues, linked to an implicit assumption that the people to be helped will be sightless, and an over-emphasis on the staff themselves learning the skills needed by visually impaired people rather than on learning how to teach these skills to people with sight problems.

In terms of specialist workers, the posts and roles of 'home teachers for the blind' were prominent in the post-war period. Home teachers were later replaced by technical officers and mobility officers. More recently these have been superseded by rehabilitation officers/workers. Although the content and organization[10] of training as such is beyond the scope of our discussion here, there is a continuing need for monitoring and evaluation of specialist training courses, building upon the critical studies carried out by NFER and BMRU.

A particular and appropriately recurring theme is the teaching of how to help visually impaired people retain, recover or develop skills. Research and practice must take account of the need to understand and be sensitive to the various elements of motivation and to their inter-relation with the various tasks involved in mobility and other daily living activities. The central place of assessment skills in work with visually impaired people, and the implications of this centrality for training, have been noted in the earlier discussion of referral, assessment and review, along with the findings of studies by the SSI and others that this has been a notable area of weakness in local authority services for this client group. Training courses also need to acknowledge the changing profile and therefore the changing needs and expectations of the visually impaired population. Some of the more recent work of the Research Centre for the Education of the Visually Handicapped listed in the Directory is particularly relevant in this context.

It is important that the fundamental work of BMRU, RCEVH and others on the various dimensions of motivation and coping, and on the ways of giving effective help, continues. It has a much wider potential relevance than may be apparent at first sight and could perhaps be broadened to relate to other client groups and service areas.

The integration of specialist work(ers) within general social care services

Another area for ongoing attention, related to training, and again following from the NFER study, is the subsequent application of specialist training in the context of future employment, i.e. within the changing contexts of social services departments and voluntary[11] organizations. There are two broad sets of issues here, and they are interwoven in the particular - though not unique - context of work with people with sight problems. The

88

first is that, as the SSI inspections and other recent Department of Health reports referred to in this book have highlighted, services for visually impaired people are somewhat marginalized in the overall demands experienced by social services departments. The second concerns the kind of training appropriate for work with people with sight problems, bearing in mind the changing profile of this group which is increasingly being acknowledged.

The authors of the NFER study and of other work reported in our review have argued that visually impaired people as a distinct client group became obscured by the post-Seebohm (DHSS, 1968) generic approach. At the same time, mobility training was gaining prominence within rehabilitation and in training for rehabilitation work, through the pioneering activities (influenced by long cane training imported from the USA) of the Midlands, later the National, Mobility Centre. Whilst basic social work training is appropriately generic, with post-qualifying specialisms available to those who wish to pursue them, apart from a three-month post-qualifying certificate course validated by the then Council for Training in Social Work which commenced in 1968 but was discontinued four years later due to low take-up (see SSI, 1988b, pp. 50-1), specialist training for work with visually impaired people has continued separately from mainstream social work education. In particular, the technical, mobility and rehabilitation officer courses referred to in the previous sub-section have never been validated by the Central Council for Education and Training in Social Work (CCETSW).[12]

Further studies of the training and subsequent experiences of specialist workers may be relevant, particularly if set alongside the perspectives of other workers with whom they are in contact and those of their clients. The support and active involvement of the agencies employing specialist workers and providing services is particularly important if any such research related to specialist training is to bear fruit.

The identification and dissemination of good practice

Crucial to staff development and training, and thence to service development, is the need to identify and learn from examples of good practice. This dimension was emphasized by Griffiths (1988) but was at best only implicit in *Caring for People* (DoH, 1989a). It is an approach to which particular kinds of research can make an important contribution. What is required is a consciously developmental orientation, working in partnership with practitioners to facilitate a learning process.

Very few examples of evaluated service initiatives were reported during our review. Although we found a good deal of evidence of practice developments, this was mostly not based on research. In addition, there were examples of collaborative reviews and strategic planning activities which might represent models of good practice.

There is a need for a systematic attempt to identify new initiatives in both planning and front-line service delivery across the country, to facilitate information exchange between them, and to analyse them critically in order to identify and disseminate elements of good practice.[13] A particular focus of such a study should be collaborative activity across agency and sector boundaries. This approach may be especially timely in fields of growing concern such as provision for people with dual sensory loss, people with multiple impairments including sight loss, and elderly people with sight and other problems.

Concluding comments

The body of material identified for the purposes of our 1989-91 review has been discussed in this chapter with reference to 'the community care agenda' as crystallized in the White Paper *Caring for People* (DoH, 1989a). The broad strategy sketched in this way remains a potential framework for national research effort concerning the social support of visually impaired people. A number of specific areas of work have been suggested, and there are doubtless many other possibilities. Many of the issues identified for further research are inter-linked. Realistically, it must be acknowledged that provision for visually impaired people is not a high priority, either for the health or the social services, nor is it an area which attracts major research resources. However, many of the issues indicated as needing further study are common across a range of client groups, so that much of the social research needed in the specific field of visual impairment, especially in the context of 'community care', would be of more general relevance.

The 'community care agenda' was not much evident in specific terms as a backdrop to the majority of research projects identified in our review. Of course, the White Paper as such did not exist at the time when agency representatives were responding to our requests for information, so that direct references to it were not to be expected. However, its themes were not fundamentally new; indeed the direction of future Government policy had been prefigured in earlier documents on visual impairment as well as in those on other areas of provision.

There is a need for further research directly associated with the planning, organization and delivery of services for visually impaired people, including the evaluation of new initiatives and the identification and dissemination of models of good practice. There is also a continuing need for more fundamental studies. Efforts should be made to close the gap between the more academic research relevant to the social support of people with sight problems and the typically local and immediately operational work done in social services departments and some voluntary bodies. This divide typifies work in this particular field as it does other areas of research around social care, where, relatedly, developments of a methodological nature (in the broadest sense) are also urgently needed. More substantively, systematic and broadly based studies directly exploring the experiences and views of visually impaired people and their carers are conspicuously required. Attention must also be given to identifying and examining initiatives spanning the health/social care interface. The identification of and response to sight problems in social support terms remains a major concern, both for practice and for research. Research priority should be given to a major study around the processes of certification (by ophthalmologists) and referral to and assessment by (or on behalf of) social services departments in the context of the new community care arrangements, in which assessment of individual need is an explicit responsibility of local authorities. Such a study should incorporate attention to users' and carers' views and those of the professionals directly involved. Some of the main issues concerning inter-agency collaboration and intra-agency organization would necessarily be illuminated. (The author and colleagues have since been pursuing research of this kind; see Postscript.)

At the beginning of this chapter, as a preface to detailed discussion, some broad generalizations were offered about the overall body of research identified by our review. These are pertinent to considering how the research agenda proposed might be taken forward. Leaving to one side as a 'special category' the significant reports produced by the RNIB and the valuable contributions of, for example, the Partially Sighted Society and the Bristol Royal Society for the Blind, it was suggested that a distinction could be made between most of the relevant research based in academic settings and the typically more parochial and/or superficial studies reported by local statutory and voluntary agencies. We observed that, in a certain sense, the former perhaps paid too little overt regard to the immediate policy agenda and the latter perhaps too much. We also indicated that in visits and discussions in the course of our review we sensed that dedicated applied researchers in academic contexts felt somewhat cut off from the field and unable to influence policy and practice, despite their genuine wish to do so.

It should be noted in this context that both the Blind Mobility Research Unit and the Research Centre for the Education of the Visually Handicapped, the two most prominent specialist academically based research institutions in this field in England, have each in recent years broadened their interests to some degree from their original *raisons d'être*. This has partly been in direct recognition of the (changing) demographic profile of the client group. These developments are evidenced by, for example, the RCEVH's enquiry into the needs of elderly visually impaired people in Birmingham [1B(o)1], and the BMRU's clear sense not only of the conceptual links between their more fundamental and their more immediately practice related work, but also of the potentially wide-ranging practical impact of their studies.

Some general features of the organizational cultures of health and social services agencies may also be relevant in thinking about how to move forward. Firstly, and at the risk of being too sweeping, the dominant perspectives of senior managers, whether in health or social services, tend to be those of overall strategy and planning.[14] Too little attention is characteristically paid by senior managers to implementation seen as a complex and *professional* front-line activity, rather than as a mechanistic 'application' of 'top-down' policy directives. Relatedly, too little effort is made to identify and learn from examples of good practice (see note 13).

Secondly, within the health service the consultant's role continues to offer the possibility of making direct links between clinical practice and the needs of individual patients on the one hand and overall service provision on the other, and thus of influencing planning and resource decisions on the basis of direct experience of a number and variety of individual situations. This is true in the field of visual impairment as in other areas. In social services departments there is rarely an equivalent coming together of detailed and current experience at different levels and the possibility of significant influence on decision making. Lest this be taken as justifying more power to the elbows of consultant ophthalmologists, it may be noted that many of the latter are typically still hampered by a traditional medical perspective, regarding their patients in a somewhat mechanistic way and their own task as primarily or exclusively one of cure or repair. Thus they may not attend adequately to the psychological dimensions of sight loss, nor to the social support elements of rehabilitation.

These speculations may go some way towards explaining the relative lack of research - and perhaps of actual collaborative or joint working - at the crucial medical/social interface regarding services and support for people with a visual impairment, particularly appropriate work concerning front-line activity.

Within the broad research community, not only academics but also colleagues based in local authorities and voluntary agencies who have carried out studies in the relevant field, there is considerable scope for developing a more substantial, coherent and collaborative national programme of research concerning the social support of visually impaired people than has existed hitherto.

The lack of such a programme in recent years probably reflects perceived general resource constraints and established priorities as between client groups. The significance of work in the neglected area of visual impairment is surely revealed in a different light if the preponderance in the overall client group of elderly people who have impaired vision but who are not blind is acknowledged, and with it the need to adopt a broader framework in relation to their care and service needs.

As stated earlier, the more academic programmes of work relevant to the social dimensions of sight loss remain valuable, not least where they are addressing fundamental issues in a way which could have practical impact and outcomes. It is also entirely appropriate for social services departments and voluntary organizations to continue to carry out small-scale studies relevant to their particular changing concerns. However, there would be value in the Department of Health seeking to co-ordinate a national research programme on a broader front, with some attempt at closer integration - or at least an exchange of information - between the commissioners/consumers and the providers of various types and 'levels' of research work. The gap which the committed academic units sense between their own work and its would-be application in the context of front-line services reflects the gap between the style and content of the two broad grouping of studies we identified: those based in academic settings and those conducted by social services departments and voluntary organizations. In turn this limits the ability of sound research to influence policy and practice.

Closer collaboration between academic researchers and individual local authorities, and with the latter's umbrella organizations, especially the ADSS, would seem to be an important part of the way forward. This applies both with regard to particular research activities and in framing an overall national research programme. The Social Services Research Group (SSRG) also has an important contribution to make in each of these contexts, not least because its membership of professional researchers includes both academics and local and health authority staff.[15]

Notes

1   The implicit reference here was to the duty to keep specific registers. One would now want to emphasize also the requirements of community care planning. The way in which community care plans address the needs of visually impaired people and the provision of services to meet them forms an important part of a study carried out by the author and colleagues and nearing completion as this book goes to press (see Postscript).

2   The 'disability movement's' fundamental criticisms of the approach taken by studies such as those of the OPCS and RNIB (see Preface and Postscript) must, however, be acknowledged.

3   Evidence so far (e.g. Hardy et al., 1993; DoH (SSI/NHSME), 1993a, 1993b; Ellis, 1993; Bewley and Glendinning, 1994) confirms this suspicion.

4   This observation, which appeared in the original text (Lovelock and Edge, 1991, p. 15) as 'The information supplied on the BD8 is of limited and varying usefulness in the context of a social care assessment', was an implicit endorsement on the authors' part of what

seemed to be a widely shared view, at least as indicated in a number of studies. It was subsequently quoted and challenged (Hill et al., 1992, p. 86), on the basis of research which was 'used to assist redrafting of the revised BD8 (1990) form' (p. 83). It is not entirely clear whether Hill and his co-authors took our remarks to refer to the old or the new form, or both. In so far as we were essentially reporting the views of others, and given the date of our survey, probably in effect the former. However that may be, our primary concern was not to resist the direction taken in revising the BD8. In fact, Hill et al.'s paper not only endorsed our recommendation for 'an evaluation of the new BD8 form' (see also the next paragraph of the main text of this book and note 5), but, perhaps to some extent unwittingly, drew attention to many of the continuing difficulties associated with referral by ophthalmologists to social services departments, where frequently such assessments as follow are undertaken by non-specialist workers.

5 We understood when reporting to the Department of Health that such a study was in the SSI's work programme for 1991. We were advised subsequently that this was not - or was no longer - the case. The Department subsequently commissioned a limited review from an outside body (Insight Management Consulting, 1994 (see Postscript)).

6 The use of *case* management' here must be noted; surprisingly it now seems somewhat odd, having been almost entirely superseded by '*care* management'. This rapid terminological evolution occurred during the period following publication of *Caring for People* (DoH, 1989a); some people used the terms almost inter-changeably, others sought to distinguish overall (care) from individual (case) matters, some thought 'case' old fashioned and inappropriate to a world of 'consumers', 'customers', and 'markets'. The short, though no doubt convoluted, history of this shift remains to be written. There was evidence that (unusually) policy had been influenced significantly by research, in the form of the *case* management experiments evaluated by the Personal Social Services Research Unit at the University of Kent, which drew on North American work and experience. But then politics, including that of language, took over. In preparing this book we have amended the original text as appropriate to reflect 1994 usage.

7 A further indication of the pace of change! 'Service provision'/'service providers' should be taken to encompass both 'sides' or elements of what, in the context of implementing the legislation, is increasingly becoming institutionalized as the division of 'purchasing and providing functions'.

8 As joint purchasing/commissioning develops (see note 7) this should provide another context for research.

9 The second volume based on the RNIB survey (Walker et al., 1992) was devoted to children.

10 See Chapter 4, including notes; also Postscript.

11 To which should now be added - or perhaps the point better expressed by reference to - 'independent sector organizations', especially as the use of service agreements gains momentum (see Postscript).

12 See Postscript for a brief update on developments as regards specialist training.

13 We have given further attention to these matters, drawing on the work of such authors as Rogers (1983) and Stocking (1985) on the diffusion of innovations, in reporting an evaluation of UK participation in the EC HELIOS programme (see Lovelock and Powell, 1994).

14 This may be said despite the fact that, certainly in social services departments, planning has never been highly developed (Wistow, 1990). Recent reports (Wistow, Leedham and Hardy, 1993; Hardy, Wistow and Leedham, 1993) based on analysing samples from the first two series of the new community care plans required under the NHS and Community Care Act 1990, suggest that planning has neither yet become 'a continuous process, within which plans are only intermittent outputs', nor 'a prospective exercise aimed at both anticipating and shaping the future' (Hardy et al., 1993, p. 61). In very few localities is there evidence that planning is 'integrated within mainstream decision making and resource allocation processes across both health and local authorities' (Hardy et al., 1993, p. 60).

15 Current discussions around the report and proposals (DoH, 1994) of an Independent Review Group set up by the Department of Health to consider future strategy in respect of research and development relevant to the personal social services provide a clear context in which to take forward the suggestions made in this chapter.

Postscript

Our 1989-91 review of recent and current research added, if indirectly, to the body of evidence of shortcomings in respect of identifying and meeting the non-medical needs of people with impaired vision: not least inadequate and inappropriate response and poor co-ordination in what is necessarily a multi-agency context. The studies reviewed re-emphasized the need for services to respond collaboratively to the fact that as well as their sight related needs, visually impaired people, especially the large majority who are elderly, typically have multiple needs, many of them shared in common with their normally sighted peers. These concerns, both long-standing and current, focus around referral to and assessment by or on behalf of social services departments, where problems have persisted despite critical comment and guidance by central government and specialist bodies.

Shore's study of social rehabilitation services in nineteen local authorities (1985) and an inspection by the Social Services Inspectorate of eight authorities (1988b), both of which featured in our review, each revealed a narrow focus by social services departments on the procedural aspects of registration, commonly with lengthy delays before contact was made and sometimes with no direct contact attempted. Organizational practice, and levels of staffing and managerial supervision, were variable within and between authorities and commonly inadequate. A limited range of very basic help was generally being offered; Shore found substantial unmet demand for social and emotional rehabilitation, including training in daily living skills, counselling, and more stimulating leisure opportunities.

This Postscript has two purposes. The first is to offer a limited update on subsequent research and research-related work relevant to the social support of visually impaired people. The second is to give brief details of a specific current study which is being conducted by the author and colleagues in CEDR. This study, which is nearing completion as this book goes to press, is directly based on the conclusions of the 1989-91 research review and has sought to pursue what the latter identified as the top priority for further work. It is examining how social services departments in England and Wales are providing for the assessment of the social support needs of visually impaired people in the context of the implementation of the NHS and Community Care Act 1990, with its emphasis on the development of 'generic' arrangements for the assessment of individual needs. Planning and conducting this study have meant that the author has maintained an awareness of related research and development activities. This provides the basis for the necessarily rather superficial update which now follows.

General update

The RNIB Needs Survey

The RNIB's *General Needs Survey* was quoted in the Preface to this book and was included in the Directory as an ongoing study [1B(o)2] at the time of our review. Volume 1 of its findings (Bruce et al., 1991), concerning adults, was published shortly after we reported to the Department of Health, with Volume 2 (Walker et al., 1992), focusing upon children, following later. Notwithstanding the important criticisms made of its approach by representatives of the disability movement (see Preface to this book), the RNIB survey's confirmation of the demographic picture is important and has made some impression - at least as information - on the minds of policy makers in Britain, at both national and local level.

Volume 1 confirms earlier findings (Cullinan, 1977; Shankland Cox Partnerships, 1985a, 1985b) on the discrepancy between the number of people registered as blind or partially sighted and the number eligible for such registration. It suggests that only twenty-three per cent of an estimated 757,000 visually impaired people living in private households in Britain and who are eligible for registration are in fact registered. Younger and blind people are most likely to be registered; only thirteen per cent of partially sighted people aged seventy-five and over are registered (Bruce et al., 1991, Table 3.14; see also Calnan, 1981).

Beyond this, one of the most significant elements of the RNIB survey may prove to be the evidence it provides (Bruce et al., 1991, pp. 271-2) for seeing the registration process as the key to getting non-medical help. The fact that a variety of social care services can be provided to unregistered people with sight loss has tended in the past to offset concern about the low rate of registration. The survey strongly suggests that involvement in the process of certification and registration is by far the most significant source of information about the help which may be available.

However, and notwithstanding this reminder of the importance of the registration process, when it comes to the services actually available the RNIB survey confirms the continued applicability of the negative pictures painted by earlier studies (e.g. Shore, 1985; SSI, 1988b). The more recent RNIB work provides further evidence, much of it from interviews with visually impaired people themselves, and on a national scale, of the inadequate management, poor organization, and low level and quality, of provision.

Social research on visual impairment based in universities

The two main academically based contributors to our original review have been contacted recently for up-to-date information on their work. The Blind Mobility Research Unit at the University of Nottingham has completed the programme of research which was ongoing at the time of our review and funded on a rolling contract by the Department of Health. This is summarily reported in a substantial reference work (Robbins (ed.), 1993) documenting all research with a bearing on 'community care' funded by the Department between 1988 and 1992. The BMRU's programme is reported there (pp. 365-78) under five headings: task analysis and objective measures of mobility, training style, assessing clients' training potential, motion vision as an independent channel, and spatial problems in the congenitally blind. A number of publications produced by BMRU staff subsequent to our review are referenced.

The Department of Health did not renew the BMRU's rolling contract beyond 1991, but instead commissioned the Unit to undertake a specific three-year project to investigate the assessment of independent living skills. This was to include developing a comprehensive checklist and piloting it in several local authorities. Some difficulty has apparently been experienced in carrying out this work, in particular in obtaining the active co-operation of social services staff during a period of intense pressure and change. The BMRU has also undertaken a study of illumination, contrast and low vision. Unit staff were understandably unhappy about the loss of the major source of funding for their more fundamental work. The failure, so far, to attract alternative resources casts doubt on the BMRU's continued existence in its current form beyond 1994-95.

Birmingham University's Research Centre for the Education of the Visually Handicapped has continued some of its long-term projects. Examples concern cognitive development and school achievement among blind and partially sighted children, the design of micro-computer software to give access on the part of visually impaired children and adults to the kinds of information routinely available to their fully sighted peers, the life-styles and needs of adults of working age and those who have retired, and methods of assessing educational and psychological functioning. Among specific projects begun by RCEVH since 1991 are an investigation of the abilities and development of neonate and other very young blind infants, the standardization of a new test of Braille reading skills, the organization and functions of multidisciplinary teams concerned with the assessment and further support of visually impaired children, and the evaluation of 'open learning' facilities for young adults in further education. Three new projects begun in 1993 concern: (i) the appraisal of visual stimulation procedures (conventional and computer based) used in schools; (ii) the design of micro-computer software related to facilitating access to the National Curriculum; and (iii) a commissioned evaluation of MOBIC, a project financed by the European Community and involving several countries, in which an orientation and navigation aid based on geo-stationary satellites is used to facilitate the independent mobility of visually impaired and elderly people.

The social sciences volume of *Current Research in Britain* (CRIB), compiled and published by Longman Cartermill (now Cartermill International Ltd) in association with the British Library, has been scanned for the years since the review was conducted, using the relevant items in the various key word indexes. The work of RCEVH, but not that of BMRU, has generally been listed. The continuing work of Spencer and his colleagues in the Department of Psychology at the University of Sheffield on the mobility training of primary-age school children, which was identified in our review, has also been included. A recent private communication from Dr Spencer indicated that his group hope to extend to the adult population the approaches and techniques they have developed. Of the thirty or so entries in CRIB each year under 'vision', 'visual handicap', 'blindness' etc., a majority have continued to be in areas of academic, often experimental, psychology, with fundamental work continuing on perception, mobility and orientation. However, the growing interest in the potential of information technology, in particular, but not exclusively, in relation to the education and social/economic integration of visually impaired people, is reflected in a small but growing number of studies. Research by Dr Sally French (more recently of the Open University), at what was at the time South Bank Polytechnic, on the differential experiences of visually impaired and normally sighted physiotherapists, and a study of the economics of cataract treatment by the Centre for Health Economics at the University of York, are other examples of social science research relevant to visual impairment undertaken in the early 1990s.

The social services research register

The Register of Current Social Services Research, published annually as one number of the journal *Social Services Research* by the Department of

Social Policy and Social Work at the University of Birmingham, is the main source of information about British studies related to the personal social services, both those carried out in social services departments themselves and, increasingly, research on similar topics based in academic and other settings. It is thus one potential indicator of trends in respect of a focus within social care research on visual impairment.

We had the impression as we completed the report on our original review that a growing number of social services departments were undertaking studies of the numbers and needs of people in their areas with dual sensory loss, or undertaking similar local exercises as part of a process of reviewing their current provision for visually impaired people in general. However, analysis of the entries in the editions of the Register for 1991, 1992, 1993 and 1994 revealed very few projects specifically concerned with visual or sensory impairment.

In addition to our then still current research review for the Department of Health, the 1991 edition of the Register included only the RCEVH work on how older people's visual skills change (see above), and the evaluative study of the quality and costs of the residential rehabilitation and further education services provided by SENSE Midlands for young people with dual sensory impairments and severe learning difficulties, commissioned by the Department of Health from the Hester Adrian Research Centre at the University of Manchester. These two projects each appear in our Directory as ongoing studies but are now complete. The studies by the Hester Adrian Research Centre, the BMRU's concluded programme, and our own review, constitute the sum total of entries specifically relevant to visual impairment in Robbins' (1993) list of research funded by the Department of Health between 1988 and 1992 with a bearing on 'community care' (p. 358, pp. 365-78, and pp. 362-4 respectively).

A further fifteen to twenty entries in the 1991 Register of Current Social Services Research were indexed as having 'physical disability' as their stated frame of reference. These mainly reported surveys of need or reviews of service organization, including some examples involving interviews with users and carers. In most cases it was unclear to what extent people with sensory or visual impairment and/or services to meet their needs were explicitly or implicitly included. The 1992 and 1993 Registers each contained eleven entries indexed as 'physical disability', including several concerning children/young people. This latter sub-group was separately identified in the index to the 1993 edition. The 1992 Register had no entries indexed as specifically concerning either visual or sensory impairment, whilst the 1993 Register had a single entry under 'sight loss': the CEDR study of social care assessment still current as this book goes to press and outlined below. In 1994 this project was indexed under 'impaired vision', along with another project based in the Department of Social Work Studies at the University of Southampton, as a result of which a computer based information system has been developed to

101

assist would-be students entering higher education. (This project in fact has been directed towards all disabled students, including, but not exclusively, those with a visual impairment.) A further nine projects were indexed in the 1994 Register as concerning 'physical disability'; none of the abstracts concerned indicated explicit attention to visual or sensory impairment.

Medical research

Research funded by the Medical Research Council, as listed in its annual Handbook, has continued to include a small number of studies indexed under 'eyes' (including 'specific parts of', 'diseases (and 'specific diseases') of'), 'vision', etc. As might be expected, the work concerned is generally of a physiological, biochemical, neurological, or psychological nature, examining the development, functioning and pathology of the visual system, including perception and motion. It is mainly located in such academic contexts as the MRC Applied Psychology Unit and the Department of Experimental Psychology, both at Cambridge, and the Department of Physiology at Oxford. One or two studies based at the Institute of Ophthalmology and of a broadly similar nature have also appeared.

This kind of research was deliberately excluded from our original review, as being essentially of a 'medical' or 'clinical' nature. Generally speaking, there is little evidence - from what is admittedly a rather superficial analysis - of any greater conceptual and/or methodological overlap during the years since our review between this and what may broadly be termed 'social' research on visual impairment. Two or three recent projects on the use of visual display units (e.g. in the Department of Psychology at the University of Dundee and at the MRC Environmental Epidemiology Unit based in Southampton), and a study of 'visual discomfort and environmental design' (Cambridge), together with some of the MRC-funded studies in experimental psychology, do, however, appear to exhibit some similarity of approach to some work reported in a social science context.

The only item included to date in the MRC's Health Services Research Programme which is of any relevance to our concerns here has been 'a clinical trial of out-patient versus in-patient cataract surgery', based at the University of Bristol. In addition, the 1991 report on work funded by the Health Promotion Trust (which is financed by the tobacco industry) listed among projects supported a comparison of routine vision screening of young children by orthoptists and health visitors.

Having noted that the research of the Institute of Ophthalmology, at least that funded by the MRC, tends to be of a clinical nature, it should be reported that some members of the College of Ophthalmologists (including at least one recent MRC grant-holder personally known to the author) are keenly aware of the importance of social factors and social support needs in relation to visual impairment. Their commitment to working with colleagues in social services departments and the major voluntary agencies was demonstrated in a multidisciplinary conference held in Southampton in June 1992, entitled 'Advances in the care of visually handicapped (sic) people: meeting medical and social needs'. The conference was jointly organized by Southampton Eye Hospital, whose medical staff (recently relocated in a brand new Eye Unit at Southampton General Hospital) are very active in the College, and the RNIB.

Comment

Thus there seems to have been little change since the time of our original review in the overall extent and nature of research relevant to the social support of visually impaired people, at least as regards studies undertaken by social services departments or in universities. Such work as there is remains sporadic and limited, with studies being carried out in only a few local authorities or academic research centres at any one time. Unfortunately, it has simply not been possible to update the picture given in the main text regarding research associated with smaller voluntary organizations, but there is no reason to suppose that major change has taken place in that sector either.

Whilst the foregoing brief overview of recent research may constitute a reasonably accurate picture, some caution is necessary in drawing conclusions based merely on scanning the indexes of selected research registers. In reflecting on the necessary qualifications which must be entered, other persistent themes resurface.

Attention has been drawn to the separation of physical and sensory disability in categorizing the subject matter of studies, especially those carried out by social services departments, and the difficulty of knowing whether some at least of the examples in the former group embody a conception of disability which includes sensory loss. On a broader canvas, the large number of studies indexed in the Register of Current Social Services Research under 'elderly', together with those grouped as 'community care', 'assessment and care management' etc. could, indeed should, in principle and in practice incorporate attention to visual impairment. However, the content of the entries themselves suggests that this is unlikely to be the case in most instances, at least if we are seeking a degree of conscious attention to the specific and special needs of visually impaired people, rather than their undifferentiated inclusion as 'disabled'. The issues involved here are of course not merely methodological; the conceptual frame of reference employed both informs and reflects the way in which social services staff - researchers and others - address the needs of disabled, including visually impaired people.

As the conduct of our original review confirmed, not all eligible studies actually feature in the annual Register of Current Social Services Research (or for that matter in the other indexes examined and referred to here). Research listings depend for their content and accuracy on the preparedness of busy people to submit information, often to a prescribed format. In social services departments, relevant work which can reasonably be seen as research on a broad interpretation, or which incorporates a research dimension or uses research skills in a developmental context, is carried out in operational, planning or development sections, as well as - sometimes rather than - by officers specifically designated or seeing themselves as researchers. Much of this is unlikely to be reported for inclusion in research registers, which are rooted in a different, more 'academic', culture.

This is part of a wider phenomenon characteristic of research and development work in social services departments, much of which fails to reach a wider audience outside the immediate locality in which it is carried out. This latter and long-standing problem is surely being exacerbated by trends already evident through the 1980s and much increased with the advent of 'community care'. Probably a majority of social services departments have by now renamed or dispersed the research sections which were established - along with these departments themselves - in response to the Seebohm Report (DHSS, 1968). The earliest tasks of the new 'social services researchers' included the collection of data in the light of the requirements of the Chronically Sick and Disabled Persons Act 1970, and they have been closely associated with the continuing development of (management) information capacities, including computer based record systems.

In the 1990s, equivalent parts of the organizational structures of social services departments are now variously labelled 'monitoring and development', 'performance review', 'planning', 'quality assurance' etc., etc. 'Inspection' and 'evaluation' also feature in this lexicon, and what had formerly been the ADSS Research Committee retitled itself the Service Evaluation, Research and Information Committee. Thus various similar or related tasks are carried out under different guises by a combination of people who were previously styled (and perhaps still think of themselves as) 'researchers', and new recruits from various backgrounds who do not see themselves as part of a 'research culture'. Many in the latter group may be unaware that they are using or need to use 'research skills' - perhaps like Moliere's *Bourgeois Gentilhomme*, who had been speaking prose all his life but had never heard the term. These and related issues are currently of considerable concern to the Social Services Research Group (SSRG), as the professional organization which seeks to represent this disparate constituency (see, for example, Wistow, 1991; Challis, 1991).

These are issues beyond the scope of the present discussion, but they are significant to an understanding of the broader context in which research relevant to the social support of visually impaired people is likely to take place. They also draw attention to the implicit links between research, evaluation, development, and indeed training.

Our original review identified very few evaluative studies of service developments. The recent scan of social services research indexes revealed similarly few, with none specifically in the field of visual impairment. We would have been particularly interested in examples of such initiatives involving social and health care agencies and voluntary organizations. As our review demonstrated, it is usually possible to identify a scattering of relevant development projects, some of them involving collaboration with health and/or voluntary agencies, if one makes systematic direct enquiries of potential informants. The collation and analysis of local authority documents on a national scale and detailed case studies in two areas, on which we have been engaged since December 1992 (see below), have added further confirmation to these impressions.

One significant omission from the Directory of projects compiled in 1989-91 was a literature review concerning visual impairment among older people (Leventhall, 1992). This was partly funded as an NHSME DHA project, with a contribution from the North West RHA, and was one of the first pieces of work carried out by the Public Health Research and Resource Centre (PHRRC), based in Salford and funded by Bolton, Salford, Trafford and Wigan Health Authorities. It was carried out 'as an aid to the purchasing of ophthalmology and other relevant services', and was therefore oriented rather more to health service provision than to social care, but it would certainly have been included in our review had we known of it. It was brought to our attention by the Principal Research Officer who had been our primary contact in the Department of Health during our study, shortly after the final version of our report had been despatched to the Department. Like ourselves, she had not previously been aware of the PHRRC review, which was the first stage of a project to assess the health and social care needs of visually disabled older people and their implications for service development (see also Harries et al., 1992). Among other things, its findings added weight to the indication given by the RNIB *General Needs Survey* (Bruce et al., 1991) of the significance of self-reporting as evidence of need and of the registration process as the key route to information about and contact with services. Further research and development work around the needs of older people with sight problems have followed (Williams, 1992; Hutchinson, 1993), involving links between health and social services agencies, voluntary organizations such as Henshaw's Society for the Blind, and the University of Salford. The Public Health Research and Resource Centre is now a collaborator, along with the Centre for Health Economics at the University of York, in the National Centre for Research and Development in Primary Care, which has recently been established at the University of Manchester.

Continuing the development theme, recent information from a senior member of the RNIB's Social Services Development Unit confirms that

RNIB has considerably extended its consultancy and advisory work with individual social services departments and other agencies in England, Wales and Northern Ireland during the early 1990s. A number of reviews and research reports have been produced from these activities. Additionally, a member of the Unit co-authored *Services for People with Visual Impairment in Gwynedd* (Welsh Office (SSI), 1991). This inspection report covered a number of areas reflected in the Unit's own general work, including: monitoring and review of existing provision; referral and assessment processes; eliciting service users' views; arrangements for inter-agency collaboration; identification of the numbers and needs of the visually impaired population; and staff development and training issues. A particular feature of the report was the inclusion of direct quotations from service users, graphically illustrating the negative effects of inadequate services on people's lives.

The Unit has also produced a 'community care training package' entitled *Reaching the Needs of People with Visual Disabilities* (RNIB, 1994), with financial support from the Department of Health.

The person most closely involved with developing the package, Pamela Williams, is also the author of a valuable chapter entitled 'Care management and assessment with blind and partially sighted people', in *Back from the Wellhouse: Discussion papers on sensory impairment and training in community care* (CCETSW, 1993, pp. 39-91). Both this chapter and the training package are referred to positively in the 1994-95 edition of *The In Touch Handbook* (Ford et al., 1994, p. 112. The commissioning of Williams' paper by the Central Council for Education and Training in Social Work, and its publication together with equivalent papers on work with deaf and hard of hearing people and people with multiple impairments as CCETSW Paper 32.1, may be taken to indicate a long overdue recognition on the part of the Council of the importance of sensory impairment.

In introducing the composite text, overall editor Andy Stevens acknowledges (CCETSW, 1993, p. 10) that 'specialist social work training provision in this area is limited at present', and that 'specialist training for welfare workers' has in fact declined during the last twenty years, due to service reorganization, resource constraint, and changes in the forms of training. However, he sees (pp. 10-11) '[t]he recent establishment of the training continuum of vocational qualifications, the Diploma in Social Work (Dip SW) and post qualifying and advanced awards' as allowing for 'a greater diversity of routes to accredited training'. He cites (p. 11) specific initiatives relating to sensory impairment, among them one DipSW programme (presumably that at Staffordshire University: see James (1993)) offering an 'area of particular practice' with 'blind people' (sic), and a group of 'voluntary organisations for blind people' seeking to establish an accredited award structure for rehabilitation and mobility officers and other staff. CCETSW has been discussing the integration of this into the NVQ structure with the group concerned and with the Care Sector Consortium. The hope is expressed (p. 11) that such initiatives 'will form the foundation for greater integration of sensory impairment issues into community care and other generic social work training', and that the papers published together as CCETSW Paper 32.1 will assist this, as well as being used by individual students and trainers.

The Department of Health's long-standing interest in training for work with visually impaired people, and in research related to such training, has featured at various points in the main body of this book. Such funds as the Department has allocated to research relevant to the social support of visually impaired people since our review have mainly been directed towards 'skills mix' and 'workforce planning'. This priority was implied in some of the detailed comments made by representatives of 'customer divisions' (i.e. officials from the relevant policy sections and from the SSI) on the draft report on our review. It was reflected in the project subsequently commissioned from the BMRU, which was rather different, as we have seen above, from the Unit's previous work.

In discussing (Chapter 4) the NFER's DoH-funded study of the main specialist training courses, the development of a unified form of training for rehabilitation officers was noted. So too was the fact that at the time the courses concerned were provided by voluntary sector organizations (the National Mobility Centre, and the North and South Regional Associations for the Blind) and located outside mainstream tertiary education. Further changes have occurred since, and the present situation remains fluid. The Department of Health modified the funding arrangements for people training as rehabilitation workers, with effect from April 1994. Before that date, changes were taking place in the organization and location of the three courses just referred to. Courses now based at the RNIB School of Rehabilitation Studies at the University of Central England, and at Leeds Metropolitan University, are variously equivalent to or replace those previously run by the NMC and NRAB respectively. NRAB no longer offers training. What was formerly the SRAB course has been run by a private company for the past two years or so, and SRAB as a whole closed during 1994. The Guide Dogs for the Blind Association has also been active for several years in training rehabilitation workers, and now provides courses accredited by the Open University.

On a more directly developmental front, and fully aware of the need for further efforts to encourage local authorities to adopt the best practice indicated in *A Wider Vision* (SSI, 1988b), *Co-ordinating Services for Visually Handicapped People* (DoH, 1989b) etc., the SSI has produced a package entitled the *Good Sense Guide* (SSI, 1991b). This consists of a booklet, a set of data collection sheets, and an 'action timetable and *aide memoire*' in the form of a fifteen-month wallchart. It is introduced as:

[A] structured way of evaluating the services offered by local authorities to people with sensory disabilities, within the framework of a one-day seminar for senior managers and elected local authority members. By posing questions and initiating debate on service provision, attitudes, and levels of need, it takes participants on a speedy tour of their own services, to enable them to look at these afresh. Its aim is to encourage a better understanding of the key issues and problems involved, and to equip participants to devise viable, effective and appropriate improvements. (p. 8)

The Ministerial Foreword to the *Good Sense Guide* refers (pp. 4-5) to the NHS and Community Care Act 1990 (and the Children Act 1989) as providing the opportunity to achieve the objective of:

enabl[ing] providers, in partnership with users and carers ..., to develop appropriate targetted services for people with sensory disabilities.

A request to the Nuffield Institute for Health's Community Care Innovative Practices Database yielded information from a small number of entries specifically relevant to visual impairment. The Norfolk Disability Information Federation, funded as part of the DoH National Disability Information Project, has considered the information needs of sensory impaired people as a specific objective. A *Guide to Services for People in Norfolk who are Visually Impaired* has been produced and will be updated annually. The Sensory Disability (Sub-)Group which produced this has also highlighted how, in terms of the information needs of people with sensory loss, 'the medium is as important as the message'. Getting On In Cleveland, a group involving Tees Health, Sensory Loss Officers from Cleveland Social Services Department, Teeside Society for the Blind, and Action for Blind People (UK), has produced an audio-tape for blind/ visually impaired people, dealing with local and national 'community care issues'. There are several other projects concerning sensory or physical disabilities on the Nuffield Institute's database, but the information recorded about them makes no specific reference to visual impairment. Following initial work assisted by funds from the Community Care Support Force, the detailed development of the database and information service has three years' NHSME/SSI funding.

Professor Olive Stevenson (1992), reviewing what she refers to as 'the latest in a series of Audit Commission publications on community care', which in its Preface states that it 'addresses the challenge to the traditional way in which social services have delivered care to vulnerable adults', has argued that:

Although [the Audit Commission's report] does not specifically refer to the needs of people with visual disability, the general thrust of the argument is clearly of relevance to such people, especially because a high proportion are elderly, often with other disabilities, whose care in the community poses serious problems to local authorities, both quantitatively and qualitatively. (p. 109)

A thoughtful Editorial in the same number of the *British Journal of Visual Impairment* also reflects on the significance for visually impaired people of the new community care arrangements. It points to the potential for improved specialized services which may flow from the requirement on local authorities to produce community care plans 'setting out the services proposed for the various client groups, including *of course* visually impaired people' (BJVI, 1992, p. 77) [emphasis added], the encouragement to 'contract out' services, and other related changes. However, as the writer of the Editorial notes (ibid.): 'How all this will work out in practice in relation to visually impaired people it is too early to say.' It is suggested that where appropriately experienced and adequately resourced and staffed voluntary agencies, perhaps already with well developed links with the statutory authorities, are available to 'take over' assessment and/or rehabilitation, positive developments are entirely feasible. However, limited resources are seen as threatening adequate provision in a number of ways:

> Given adequate funding and the adjustments that experience could bring, Community Care might have been - and might still be - one of the many possible moves towards overcoming some of the all too familiar problems of visual impairment ... What lies immediately ahead [however,] is the difficulty of "attempting to square the circle between needs, targets and resourses" (sic) (BJVI, 1992, p. 78, quoting Audit Commission, 1992)

We had understood - although the statement to this effect in our report was corrected by a member of the SSI who would certainly have known the current situation in this regard - that a study of the impact on local policy and practice of the recommendations contained in *Co-ordinating Services for Visually Handicapped People* (DoH, 1989b) was to form part of the Inspectorate's 1991 work programme. The specific inspection in Gwynedd (Welsh Office (SSI), 1991), to which we have already referred, certainly indicated that in that local authority area at least the themes of *Co-ordinating Services* ... had not been fully taken on board. More recently, the Department commissioned a review specifically of the current process of certification using the revised (1990) version of Form BD8. Undertaking this brief, Insight Management Consulting examined the practices of both health and social services staff in six areas of England. The recently published report (1994) suggests that the depressing general picture painted in *A Wider Vision* (SSI, 1988b) has not greatly changed.

Further, in addition to the persisting operational difficulties around certification and registration, and notwithstanding the reasons for and conduct of the review and revision of Form BD8 in 1990, there continues to be disagreement about what information the BD8 should or does convey to social services departments, and what use the latter do or might put it to (Hill et al., 1992) and a common failure, even among ophthalmologists (Thomas, 1991; Rumney, 1992), to distinguish between certification and registration.

All of which brings us to the study which the present writer and colleagues are currently undertaking to put into effect the main recommendations flowing from the earlier research review.

Visual impairment, assessment, and community care

Our review concluded that the priority area for further research relevant to the provision of social support to people with visual impairments was a comprehensive study of the process(es) of referral to and assessment by or on behalf of social services departments, as the central part of an attempt to understand how and why services to meet individuals' needs 'come together' or not in particular areas. Crucial to this would be making good one of the gaps in previous research in terms of attention to the views and experiences of visually impaired people themselves and of their informal carers, and setting these alongside the views of front-line staff in different agency contexts working directly with them.

The Department of Health received the report on our research review (Lovelock and Edge, 1991) positively. However, it was fairly clear that whatever research resources might be made available in the next period for work relating to social care for visually impaired people, an extended, and in the best sense academic study along the lines we proposed was unlikely to be funded by the Department. One reason for this may have been the apparent - and understandable - weariness which officials in the relevant sections of the Department, including the SSI, seemed to feel at the prospect of yet another effort to exhort social services departments to do better, and yet another attempt to identify models of good practice, which they felt simply did not exist at local level. Some of the main areas in which the Department's research resources have subsequently been directed have been indicated earlier in this Postscript.

Nevertheless, we have been able to conduct a study along the lines we identified as having high priority, and certain aspects of its context may bear repeating here. It is nearing completion as this book goes to press.

Whilst some services are mandatory, such as maintaining a register of people to whom Section 29 of the National Assistance Act 1948 applies, including blind and partially sighted people, a much wider range of services are the duty of the local authority to provide if it is satisfied that there is a need. In some localities there is a long tradition of appropriate voluntary organizations not only providing services on their own account, but of doing so explicitly on behalf of the local authority, on an agency basis; this can include administering the process of registration.

110

It is important to distinguish between the closely linked processes of certification and registration, which are often confused in discussion, even by the professionals closely involved (Thomas, 1991; Rumney, 1992). A certificate of blindness or partial sight (Form BD8 (revised 1990)) is completed by an ophthalmologist (usually a consultant) following an eye examination indicating *inter alia* the degree of visual impairment. The patient's signed consent is required for a copy of the relevant sections of the BD8 (Parts 1-4) to be forwarded to the appropriate social services department. The confusion between certification and registration is encouraged by the fact that Part 5 of the BD8 (a section without the name of the individual concerned) is sent to OPCS for statistical purposes.

Registration generally follows receipt of the BD8 by the social services department, but registration is not only not synonymous with certification, neither is it - or should it be - automatic upon receipt of a BD8. Registration is voluntary and in this context the BD8 is, strictly, a certificate of eligibility for registration. Registration as blind is necessary in order to qualify for some services, particularly certain financial benefits and concessions. However, a recent communication from an official within the Department of Health indicates that in fact the Inland Revenue will now (since Summer 1994) accept evidence of certification as sufficient in deciding entitlement to the Blind Person's Tax Allowance. People registered as partially sighted, and also, significantly, unregistered people with needs related to limited sight, are anyway eligible for a variety of help and advice from social services departments. *Co-ordinating Services for Visually Handicapped People* (DoH, 1989b) firmly states what would be regarded widely as appropriate practice:

> A representative of the social services department, either a qualified social worker with experience in visual handicap or a worker specialising in services for visually handicapped people, should contact the client quickly after certification to discuss the perceived needs for services and, if appropriate, to carry out a comprehensive assessment. (p. 9, para. 3.15.2)

As we have seen, whilst participation in the registration process is the most important source of information about the help available to people with sight problems and the key route to accessing services (Bruce et al., 1991), the operation of this process has long been (Shore, 1985; SSI, 1988b) and remains (Insight Management Consulting, 1994) unsatisfactory in many parts of the country.

Section 47(2) of the NHS and Community Care Act 1990 explicitly confirms the provision of the Disabled Persons (Services, Consultation and Representation) Act 1986, under which local authorities must assess the needs of people who are disabled in the terms of the National Assistance Act 1948, including visually impaired people, for the services listed in Section 2 of the Chronically Sick and Disabled Persons Act 1970 (i.e. those services which the local authority must ensure are provided to meet the requirements of the 1948 Act).

One of the six key policy objectives stated in *Caring for People* (DoH, 1989a) was 'to make proper assessment of need and good case management the cornerstone of high quality care' (p. 5). The NHS and Community Care Act 1990 of course applies across the 'priority groups' and therefore includes disabled people in general and visually impaired people in particular. However, given the history of low priority and inadequate provision afforded to the latter group, and the undeniable influence on the thinking behind recent legislation of the soaring cost to the public purse of private sector residential care for elderly people, it seemed unlikely that visually impaired people and their social support needs would be uppermost in the minds of local authority managers and planners as they addressed the implementation of the new arrangements. These concerns were given substance by a reading of emerging DoH guidance on care management and assessment (DoH, 1990; DoH/Scottish Office, 1991; SSI, 1991a), which contained scarcely any reference to visual impairment: something of an irony when the large majority of people with sight loss are elderly. At the same time, this draws attention to the core problem of how to acknowledge and respond flexibly to the needs of specific groups and individuals within the overall 'generic' framework of provision.

Like the Disabled Persons Act 1986, the NHS and Community Care Act is explicitly concerned with choice and user-led service provision. Certain sections of the 1986 Act, in particular those giving a disabled person the right to employ a representative or advocate in dealing with statutory authorities, crucially in relation to the assessment of individual needs, and to receive a written statement of such assessed needs, have not been implemented. The Government's contention that the NHS and Community Care Act renders such implementation unnecessary has been a matter of great concern to those directly affected and to their representatives (Clarke, 1991; Sutton, 1991). The more recent legislation explicitly seeks to link choice with cost-effectiveness, through the mechanisms of assessment and care management. Considerable doubt has been expressed about the likelihood of the Act leading to significant advance in terms of the empowerment of service users and carers, particularly in the context of assessment. For example, Smale and his colleagues (Smale and Tuson, 1993; Smale et al., 1994) note the tendency for social services departments to concentrate on organizational changes and to fail to learn from examples of front-line innovation. The argument is supported, *inter alia*, by recent empirical work on user involvement and empowerment (Beresford and Croft, 1986, 1990; Marsh and Fisher, 1992).

Thus further research around the processes by which visually impaired people are referred to social services departments, offered an assessment, and provided with social support services, remained a high priority. The long-standing concerns associated with the certification/registration process demanded re-examination specifically in the new context of the (delayed) implementation of those aspects of the NHS and Community Care Act concerned with assessment, which require local authorities to develop and make public detailed arrangements for assessing the needs of people in their areas.

Would the shortfalls of the pre-existing system be remedied or exacerbated? Would visually impaired people be more or less likely to gain access - if they so wished - to an appropriate assessment of their social care needs? How would the existing BD8 procedures be integrated into the new 'generic' assessment arrangements for community care? The requirement that a doctor of consultant status certifies eligibility for registration is unique to visual impairment. Would BD8s be seen and treated as referrals in the same way as other requests or recommendations for possible help, following appropriate assessment? Or would they - and thence the visually impaired people and front-line staff immediately involved - remain 'special' only in an administrative sense and marginalized in terms of priority?

With funding from the Joseph Rowntree Foundation, research to investigate these and related issues commenced in December 1992. Briefly stated, the formal aims of the study are:

To examine in detail the policies, organizational arrangements and practices adopted by social services departments for assessing the social support needs of people with impaired vision.

To explore how these arrangements have changed following the introduction of the NHS and Community Care Act 1990.

To understand and contrast the perspectives of the several parties involved in the activities and processes surrounding assessment.

To analyse the obstacles to 'best practice' in this area, and to identify and disseminate positive models and examples of innovatory initiatives.

The research design has involved two linked phases:

Phase 1 Collation and analysis of community care plans and specialist policy and operational documents concerning visual impairment, obtained from social services departments throughout England and Wales, to gain a national overview.

Phase 2 Detailed case studies in two contrasting local authority areas: interviews with 'key informants' at strategic and operational levels in several agencies; 'tracking' individuals via agency data on referral and assessment to identify the patterns by which services are accessed; interviews with visually impaired people, carers, and front-line workers carrying out assessments.

113

Two other studies funded by the Rowntree Foundation, both recently completed, complement our own current work. Among the issues addressed by the first, based at the University of Birmingham, was whether the 1986 Disabled Persons Act or the 1990 NHS and Community Care Act provides the main reference point for social workers and their managers in relation to assessing the needs of disabled people. The apt title of the report on this research, *Squaring the Circle* (Ellis, 1993), reflects what is perhaps its central finding: that the assessment process is essentially the locus of rationing scarce resources. There is ample demonstration of the direct influence of resource constraints on the nature of assessment, which remains 'unavoidably' service-led. The emphasis on targeting contained in government policy effectively blocks any wish on the part of professional workers to approach the assessment task in an empowering fashion and to respond to individual need comprehensively and in terms of overall quality of life. A perhaps surprisingly high proportion of the individual case studies referred to in Ellis's report concern people with sight-related problems - often amongst other needs. These examples graphically illustrate a widespread failure to acknowledge the emotional dimension of sight loss and the provision of inappropriate or inadequate forms of help. In one area, response to BD8 referrals automatically involved a five-month delay.

A study of the involvement of organizations of and for disabled people in the community care planning process (Bewley and Glendinning, 1994), based at the University of Manchester, has shown that although summaries of the first (i.e. the 1992-93) plans were sometimes produced in Braille, on tape, and/or in languages other than English, the heavy reliance on written (English) in consultation documents either excluded people with visual impairments (among other minority groups) or increased the costs to individuals or organizations who had themselves to arrange and resource the production of material in suitable formats. People with sensory impairments were among the groups most likely to be excluded from the process by the failure of local authorities to recognize the importance of 'outreach' work: i.e. providing sufficient and appropriate information, support, and resources to enable disabled people to make a mutually valuable contribution to the development of plans and services.

In the first phase of our own study we have analysed a combination of 1992-93 and 1993-94 community care plans, covering virtually all social services departments in England and Wales. Our focus was on those sections of the plans which discussed the needs of visually impaired people and services to meet them, and those sections setting out overall arrangements for the assessment of individual needs. Additional specialist documentation supplied by roughly half the responding departments has provided supplementary information, for example on the organization of services for visually impaired people.

The national overview emerging from this analysis suggests that in very

114

many areas visual impairment remains a low priority. The system of certification and registration using Form BD8 generally appears not to have been acknowledged in the new 'generic' assessment arrangements for 'community care'. Thus the long-standing problems surrounding BD8 procedures in all probability persist, including those relating to the availability, if appropriate, of a comprehensive assessment of social care needs, with the promise of 'community care' for visually impaired people remaining to that extent unfulfilled.

These tentative but critical conclusions are mutually supportive of the findings of other recently published work, in particular joint SSI/NHSME studies on community care plans, on assessment, and on implementing community care for younger people with physical and sensory disabilities (Hardy et al., 1993; DoH (SSI/NHSME), 1993a, 1993b). These three studies were amongst the first six published from the series of fourteen exercises monitoring the first year of the (full) implementation of 'community care'.

There is a need for some caution in interpreting the findings from Phase 1 of our own study. Beyond an evident lack of detailed attention to visual impairment in many community care plans, much rests on the apparently limited degree of connection between various parts of these documents. Important as this finding is, it no doubt essentially reflects the fact (not without its own significance) that these plans are typically collated from separate elements originally prepared by different (groups of) authors. The production of 'a good plan' (begging the question here of the appropriate criteria for such an accolade) would anyway indicate 'merely' the ability of the responsible agency/ies to produce a document of given quality. It would not necessarily indicate the quality of the planning process itself; nor, in turn, would it necessarily reflect the reality of service delivery and receipt 'on the front line'.

The more detailed examination of the key issues around referral and social care assessment which we have been undertaking in Phase 2 of our research will help to clarify further the rapidly changing current situation. Case studies have been completed in two local authorities, differing in a number of ways, including in terms of the patterns of service organization evident in each. One case study site is a shire county in Southern England, which has one major and two more modest service agreements with voluntary organizations as its means of providing rehabilitation services for visually impaired people. These arrangements are in various stages of evolution. The other site is a metropolitan borough in the North of England, whose social services department remains the main provider of rehabilitation services. In both areas the local authority has retained registration and assessment functions. A specialist sensory impairment team covers the whole of the metropolitan borough; a variety of patterns of organization pertain in the various areas of the shire county. The findings of the overall study will be disseminated in a variety of ways during 1995.

By focusing on visual impairment, this new study aims to help raise the profile of a group of people whose needs have remained a low priority in resource terms and in the attention given to them in policy, practice and research contexts. Conducted from an academic base, the research addresses the major points emerging from our 1988-91 review, both in terms of its substantive content and with regard to bridging the divide identified between relevant work in university contexts and that based in local authorities and voluntary organizations. Through its evaluative and developmental orientation it is seeking to link research, policy and practice. As part of this, and actively encouraged by the Joseph Rowntree Foundation, the Project Advisory Group has among its members an Assistant Director of Social Services, an Inspector from the SSI, a consultant ophthalmologist, a senior member of the RNIB Social Services Development Unit, a representative of another major organization of visually impaired people, and two academics with long-standing interests in the field. Three of these seven people are themselves visually impaired.

The specific focus of the research is the accessibility to visually impaired people of an appropriate social care assessment, whether via the 'special' - though problematic - route to social care services afforded by the certification and registration process or via the 'generic' assessment arrangements being established under 'community care'. In examining these processes the study is illuminating some of the central issues and themes of the new community care arrangements. Among these are the assessment of individual need, community care planning, collaboration at all levels between statutory social and health care services and the independent sector, and giving a voice to service users and carers. The research is exploring these aspects of the changing scene from the perspectives of the several parties involved, including managers, front-line workers, visually impaired people, and informal carers. The study is addressing the challenge - too easily submerged - of how to ensure that the needs of special groups are addressed within a generic framework. In so-doing, in addition to its particular significance for visually impaired people and those working with them, it has a much wider relevance for the development of high quality community care.

Appendix
DIRECTORY OF RESEARCH RELEVANT TO THE SOCIAL SUPPORT OF VISUALLY IMPAIRED PEOPLE

Notes

1   See Chapter 2, especially pages 19-24, for a full discussion of the criteria for including projects in this Directory, relevant definitional and boundary issues, the rationale behind the organization of the Directory into sections, and the associated numbering system.

2   As explained in the main text, it has not been possible to update the detail of entries in the Directory. The term 'ongoing' denotes the status of the project concerned at the time details were submitted and the information included reflects this. A small number of amendments were made at the point when the Directory was **initially** finalized (i.e. during early 1991).
    Except in project titles, direct quotations, and the names of organizations, terms such as 'handicap', '(the) handicapped', 'for the blind' etc. have been amended to conform with current preferences. In this respect the Directory follows the practice adopted in revising the main text for publication in book form.
    Every effort has been made to check and where necessary to revise contact addresses and telephone numbers for the researcher(s) and/or organizations responsible for particular projects, so that readers wishing to do so may seek additional information. Complete accuracy, even at the time this book goes to press, cannot, however, be guaranteed. Some post-codes are almost certainly out-of-date. Telephone numbers given reflect the new area codes which came into operation alongside the previous codes on 1 August 1994 and which will be the only ones available for use from 16 April 1995.
    In cases where an individual is known to have moved or an organization to have changed its address, the contact information given is that which seems likely to prove most useful to anyone wishing to seek further details of a project from the person(s) directly involved. Where a contact name (e.g. of a Secretary) was originally given for a voluntary organization whose contact address is known to have changed, but no up-to-date contact name is available, only the latest known address of the organization is given. Where an organization is known to have restructured substantially in ways significant to one or more entries (e.g. The Training Agency (Employment Department Group)), or even to have ceased to exist (e.g. SRAB), the relevant entry/ies have been left unaltered. The alternative was obviously deletion of the relevant projects, which seemed inappropriate. Readers wishing to follow up any of these (or indeed other) projects should pursue their own lines of enquiry; the author may be able to assist.

3   A summary list of the projects included in the Directory follows, in the numbered order in which they appear. Projects relevant to one section but whose main entry appears in another section are indicated. Two further indexes follow the sixty-nine full entries: an index of organizations with projects listed and an alphabetical index of project titles.

Contents of Directory

and *Planning Group/Partially Sighted Society* [p. 141]

1A(c)7 Visually Disabled Services in Tameside, *Social Services Department, Tameside Metropolitan Borough Council/RNIB* [p. 143]

1A(c)8 'Working Together: The Scope for Improving Working Links between RNIB and Local Societies for the Blind', *RNIB* [p. 145]

Ongoing

1A(o)1 Aspects of Disability, *Social Services Department, Humberside County Council* [p. 147]

1A(o)2 Review of Services for People with a Visual Disability, *Social Services Department, Buckinghamshire County Council* [p. 149]

1A(o)3 Strategic Framework 1991-2001, *Bedfordshire Joint Care Planning Team* [p. 151]

Also relevant to Section 1A

1B(c)1 'The Client's View: Social and Rehabilitation Services', *Partially Sighted Society* [p. 153]

2(o)1 Low Vision Services in Avon, *Bristol Royal Society for the Blind/ Social Services Department, Avon County Council* [p. 179]

1B   Client based surveys of need

Completed

1B(c)1 'The Client's View: Social and Rehabilitation Services', *Partially Sighted Society* [p. 153]

1B(c)2 Transport Facilities for the Visually Impaired in Bristol, *Bristol Royal Society for the Blind* [p. 155]

1B(c)3 Visually Handicapped People in Hampshire: A Survey of Needs, *Sight Concern Hampshire, Hampshire Association for the Care of the Blind* [p. 157]

Ongoing

1B(o)1 The Elders Project: A Longitudinal Enquiry, *Research Centre for the*

Education of the Visually Handicapped, University of Birmingham [p. 159]

1B(o)2   General Needs Survey, *RNIB* [p. 161]

1B(o)3   Prevention of Blindness: An Examination of Changing Patterns of Care and the Impact on Sight Loss, *Bristol Royal Society for the Blind* [p. 163]

1B(o)4   Survey and Review of Needs, *Department of Social Services and Housing, London Borough of Bromley/Kent Association for the Blind* [p. 165]

1B(o)5   Survey of Needs: Visually Impaired People of Cambridgeshire, *Cambridgeshire Society for the Blind and Partially Sighted* [p. 167]

1B(o)6   Survey of Needs of Visually Impaired People Within the Ten Districts Covered by the Chester Blind Welfare Society, *Chester Blind Welfare Society* [p. 169]

Also relevant to Section 1B

1A(c)6   Services for People with a Visual Impairment, *South Devon Review and Planning Group/Partially Sighted Society* [p. 141]

1C   Evaluations of service initiatives

Completed

1C(c)1   'Operation Cataract': Operations on a Day Care Basis with Hotel After-Care, *Impact Foundation/Worthing District Health Authority* [p. 171]

Ongoing

1C(o)1   Evaluation Study of an Adviser/Counsellor Based at an Eye Hospital, *Brighton Society for the Blind* [p. 173]

Also relevant to Section 1C

1A(c)4   The Registration and Continuing Care of People with a Visual Impairment, *Bristol Royal Society for the Blind/Social Services Department, Avon County Council* [p. 137]

Section 2   Low vision/partial sight

Completed

Ongoing

Also relevant to Section 2

Section 3   Mobility

Completed

Ongoing

3(o)1   Mobility Aids for Visually Impaired People, *Bristol Royal Society for the Blind* [p. 191]

3(o)2   Mobility Related Feelings and the Walking Speed of Visually Impaired Travellers, *Blind Mobility Research Unit* [p. 193]

3(o)3   Obstacle Location Without Vision, *Blind Mobility Research Unit* [p. 195]

3(o)4   Preliminary Comparison of Expert and Poor Travellers' Abilities to Cope with Independent Travel, *Blind Mobility Research Unit* [p. 197]

3(o)5   Task Analysis of Mobility, *Blind Mobility Research Unit* [p. 199]

3(o)6   Use of Maps and Graphics in the Mobility Training of Young Visually Handicapped Children, *Department of Psychology, University of Sheffield* [p. 201]

3(o)7   Visual Balance Control, *Blind Mobility Research Unit* [p. 203]

Also relevant to Section 3

2(c)1   The Development of Measures of Low Vision Mobility Performance, *Blind Mobility Research Unit* [p. 175]

4(c)3   Investigation of Mobility Officers' Assessments of Clients' Needs for Training, *Blind Mobility Research Unit* [p. 209]

4(c)4   Low Vision Assessment and Training, *Blind Mobility Research Unit* [p. 211]

4(c)6   Role Play of Different Training Styles, *Blind Mobility Research Unit* [p. 215]

2(o)2   Motion Vision in the Partially Sighted, *Blind Mobility Research Unit* [p. 181]

Section 4   **Training of specialist staff, and assessment and training of visually impaired people**

Completed

4(c)1   Evaluation of Assessment Procedures at the RNIB Rehabilitation Centre, Torquay, *Blind Mobility Research Unit, University of Nottingham* [p. 205]

4(c)2   Identification of Potential Confusions in Lesson Analysis Schedule, *Blind Mobility Research Unit* [p. 207]

4(c)3   Investigation of Mobility Officers' Assessments of Clients' Needs for Training, *Blind Mobility Research Unit* [p. 209]

4(c)4   Low Vision Assessment and Training, *Blind Mobility Research Unit* [p. 211]

4(c)5   The Manual Dexterity of Visually Handicapped Adults, *Research Centre for the Education of the Visually Handicapped, University of Birmingham* [p. 213]

4(c)6   Role-Play of Different Training Styles, *Blind Mobility Research Unit* [p. 215]

4(c)7   'Beyond Vision: Training for Workers in Visual Impairment', *National Foundation for Educational Research* [p. 217]

Ongoing

4(o)1   Access to Information and Learning by Visually Handicapped People Through Micro-Computer Technology, *Research Centre for the Education of the Visually Handicapped* [p. 219]

4(o)2   Evaluation of a Low Vision Training Programme, *Partially Sighted Society* [p. 221]

4(o)3   Psychological Adjustment to Sight Loss, *Blind Mobility Research Unit* [p. 223]

4(o)4   Using Sighted Volunteers for Teaching Moon to Newly Blinded Adults, *Research Centre for the Education of the Visually Handicapped* [p. 225]

4(o)5   Welfare of the Visually Impaired: Daily Living Skills and Independence, *Surrey Voluntary Association for the Blind* [p. 227]

Also relevant to Section 4

1A(c)6 Services for People with a Visual Impairment, *South Devon Review and Planning Group/Partially Sighted Society* [p. 141]

1B(c)1 'The Client's View: Social and Rehabilitation Services', *Partially Sighted Society* [p. 153]

2(c)1 The Development of Measures of Low Vision Mobility Performance, *Blind Mobility Research Unit* [p. 175]

3(c)2 Investigation of Mobility Related Feelings, *Blind Mobility Research Unit* [p. 185]

3(c)4 Spatial Representation and Congenital Blindness, *Blind Mobility Research Unit* [p. 189]

1B(o)1 The Elders Project: A Longitudinal Enquiry, *Research Centre for the Education of the Visually Handicapped* [p. 159]

2(o)2 Motion Vision in the Partially Sighted, *Blind Mobility Research Unit* [p. 181]

3(o)2 Mobility Related Feelings and the Walking Speed of Visually Impaired Travellers, *Blind Mobility Research Unit* [p. 193]

3(o)3 Obstacle Location Without Vision, *Blind Mobility Research Unit* [p. 195]

3(o)4 Preliminary Comparison of Expert and Poor Travellers' Abilities to Cope with Independent Travel, *Blind Mobility Research Unit* [p. 197]

3(o)5 Task Analysis of Mobility, *Blind Mobility Research Unit* [p. 199]

3(o)6 Use of Maps and Graphics in the Mobility Training of Young Visually Handicapped Children, *Department of Psychology, University of Sheffield* [p. 201]

3(o)7 Visual Balance Control, *Blind Mobility Research Unit* [p. 203]

Section 5   Dual sensory impairment

Completed

5(c)1   'Breaking Through: Developing Services for Deaf-Blind People', *Deaf-Blind Services Liaison Group* [p. 229]

5(c)2   Feasibility Study for a County-Wide Service for Deaf-Blind People, *Social Services Department, Norfolk County Council* [p. 231]

5(c)3   Review of Services for Hearing Impaired and Visually Handicapped People, *Directorate of Housing and Personal Services, London Borough of Bexley* [p. 233]

Ongoing

5(o)1   Deaf-Blind Services in Avon, *Bristol Royal Society for the Blind* [p. 235]

5(o)2   Evaluation of SENSE Midlands (Further Education), *Hester Adrian Research Centre, University of Manchester* [p. 237]

5(o)3   Identifying Needs and Numbers of Deaf-Blind in Devon, *Social Services Department, Devon County Council/SENSE South West* [p. 239]

5(o)4   Provision of Services for Deaf-Blind People, *Sunderland and Durham County Incorporated Royal Institution for the Blind* [p. 241]

5(o)5   Review and Survey of the Provision of Services to People who are Deaf-Blind, *Social Services Division, Stockport Metropolitan Borough Council* [p. 243]

Also relevant to Section 5

6(c)2   Mentally Handicapped People with Hearing and Sight Problems, *Social Services Department, Cornwall County Council* [p. 247]

Section 6   Multiple impairment including sight loss

Completed

6(c)1   Day Care for Visually Impaired People with Learning Difficulties, *Bristol Royal Society for the Blind* [p. 245]

4(o)4   Using Sighted Volunteers for Teaching Moon to Newly Blinded Adults, *Research Centre for the Education of the Visually Handicapped* [p. 225]

5(o)2   Evaluation of SENSE Midlands (Further Education), *Hester Adrian Research Centre, University of Manchester* [p. 237]

Note: The Research Centre for the Education of the Visually Handicapped at the University of Birmingham has been involved for many years in a wide range of studies relating to the special educational needs of visually impaired people, both adults and children. This work has addressed both formal education and acquiring skills to compensate for the loss of the ability to read printed matter. It ranges from the analysis of teaching techniques to the development of micro-computer technology. A major project not included in the listing is the longitudinal investigation of cognitive development and school achievement in visually impaired pupils, begun in 1973. A full list of publications from this work is available from RCEVH. Recent publications particularly relevant to this review are:

Tobin, M.J. (1987), 'Special and mainstream schooling: some teenagers' views', *New Beacon*, vol. 71, no. 837, pp. 3-6.

Tobin, M.J. and Hill, E.W. (1988), 'Visually impaired teenagers: ambitions, attitudes and interests', *Journal of Visual Impairment & Blindness*, vol. 82, no. 12, pp. 414-16.

Tobin, M.J. and Hill, E.W. (1989), 'The present and the future: concerns of visually impaired teenagers', *British Journal of Visual Impairment*, vol. 7, no. 2, pp. 55-7.

Section 8   Employment

Completed

8(c)1   Employment Services for the Visually Handicapped: 'Six-Month Survey', *Psychological Services Branch, The Training Agency* [p. 259]

8(c)2   Employment Services for the Visually Handicapped: 'Eighteen-Month Survey and Final Report', *Psychological Services Branch, The Training Agency* [p. 261]

8(c)3   'A Sense of Purpose: A Study of Visually Handicapped People and their Search for Work', *RNIB* [p. 263]

Ongoing

8(o)1   Employment Rehabilitation Feasibility Studies, *RNIB* [p. 265]

8(o)2   Vocational Opportunities for the Visually Impaired with Manual and Allied Skills, *RNIB* [p. 267]

Also relevant to Section 8

4(c)1   Evaluation of Assessment Procedures at the RNIB Rehabilitation Centre, Torquay, *Blind Mobility Research Unit, University of Nottingham* [p. 205]

AUDIT OF SERVICES FOR PEOPLE WITH VISUAL HANDICAPS

Researcher(s):   John Windebank
                  Tel: 01273 481252

                  Roger Lambert and Judi Dettmar
                  Tel: 01273 481275

                  Social Services Department
                  East Sussex County Council
                  PO Box 5, County Hall
                  St Anne's Crescent
                  Lewes, East Sussex BN7 1SW

Abstract:

Aims: To investigate and comment upon the range and nature and the co-ordination and partnership arrangements of all services for people with visual impairments in the County, whether supplied by the County Council, the voluntary organizations, or other statutory agencies, and to make recommendations as to how the services may be developed effectively.

Methods: In-depth interviews with service managers, service providers, national and local voluntary organizations, health representatives and a small sample of users. Analysis of available quantitative and financial data, including the appropriate registers. Small sample of users but main emphasis on organizations and management information.

Current status: Completed.

Summary of findings:

Report not available until permission given by Department.

Subjects of study:	All ages, including children. Blind and partially sighted people, whether registered or not.
Coverage:	County of East Sussex.
Timescale:	1 September 1989 - 1 January 1990.
Cost:	£15,000.
Funding body/bodies:	'In-house' project.
Report(s):	Confidential. Departmental Management Team accepted the recommendations in the report, but action was deferred whilst consideration was given to the implications of the White Paper *Caring for People* (DoH, 1989a). Limited circulation within the Department; not yet generally available.

BLIND AND PARTIALLY SIGHTED PEOPLE IN HARLOW: AN EXAMINATION OF THE NUMBER AND CIRCUMSTANCES OF, AND THE SERVICES PROVIDED TO, BLIND AND PARTIALLY SIGHTED PEOPLE IN THE HARLOW DISTRICT

Researcher(s):   Andrew Rust
Research Officer
Social Services Department
Essex County Council
PO Box 297, County Hall
Chelmsford, Essex CM1 1YS
Tel: 01245 492211

Abstract:

Aims: This research was carried out as part of a research evaluation of the feasibility and potential of a computerized register of physically disabled people in the County of Essex. The Department also wanted to examine the circumstances of and services provided to this group of clients, and to demonstrate the feasibility of carrying out more detailed studies using the register as a sampling frame.

Methods: As the time this exercise would take was unknown, only a small sub-group of blind and partially sighted registrations was selected to enter on the computer.

Current status: Completed.

Summary of findings:

Transferring information from manual to computerized records averaged forty records per day.

Majority of clients females over the age of retirement and likely to be living alone. Mobility decreased with age rather than sight problems. Of those aged under twenty-five, only one lived independently. Thirty-five per cent were in current contact with Social Services Department during previous ten months, but sixteen per cent had had no contact since 1981. Registration was the most frequent reason for contact; equipment delivery next highest, with the most common equipment white stick and bath aids.

Specialist worker for visually impaired provided most contact.
Information stored on computer makes analysis of client sub-groups possible and access is quicker than via manual records.

Subjects of study:	260 clients: 60 per cent female, 40 per cent male; 65 per cent over 65 yrs, 83 per cent over 40, 8 children under 16 yrs.
Coverage:	Sample sub-group of registered blind and partially sighted people in Harlow. Part of a much larger feasibility study on the registration of all physically disabled people with Essex County SSD.
Timescale:	Research carried out during 1987.
Cost:	
Funding body/bodies:	'In-house' project.
Report(s):	Report obtainable from Social Services Department, Essex County Council.

LOCAL AUTHORITY SOCIAL REHABILITATION SERVICES TO VISUALLY HANDICAPPED PEOPLE

Researcher(s):   Penelope Shore
c/o Royal National Institute for the Blind
224 Great Portland Street
London W1N 6AA
Tel: 0171 388 1266

Abstract:

Survey of nineteen local authorities in England and Wales on behalf of RNIB as part of a wider review of its 'future role in the development and provision of rehabilitation'.

Aims: To test prevailing assumptions about the nature of local authority provision of social rehabilitation services for visually impaired adults, including the expectation that standards would vary between authorities, that they would be less sophisticated in rural authorities, and that clients and their authorities prefer local to residential rehabilitation services.

Methods: Stratified random sample. Phase 1: postal questionnaire to local authority SSDs on staffing levels and numbers of people registered. Phase 2: interviews/discussions with staff of SSDs. Phase 3: interviews with sample of visually impaired people drawn from the nineteen local authorities.

Current status: Completed.

Summary of findings:

Evidence generally confirmed assumptions outlined in aims. Unequal distribution of resources within and between authorities. Rural authorities are not 'less sophisticated', but face different problems in organizing and delivering services. Other findings include: 'ageist attitudes' in the provision of services; a prevalent lack of early intervention; widespread variation in attitudes towards counselling; and a need to develop better leisure and recreational opportunities.

Recommendations: To RNIB: development of services to reflect the priorities for service needs and policy identified by the local authorities and DHSS; further research to improve services; development of services on a regional basis; proper recognition of the needs of visually impaired people who are elderly.

Subjects of study: See Abstract.

Coverage:

Timescale: 1983 - 1985.

Cost:

Funding body/bodies:

Report(s):   Shore, P. (1985), *Local Authority Social Rehabilitation Services to Visually Handicapped People,* RNIB, London. ('The Shore Report'.)

THE REGISTRATION AND CONTINUING CARE OF PEOPLE WITH A VISUAL IMPAIRMENT

Researcher(s):   David Thomas (Avon SSD)
c/o Bristol Royal Society for the Blind
Stillhouse Lane
Bedminster, Bristol BS3 4EB
Tel: 0117 923 0060 (Bristol Eye Hospital)

(in association with Avon Social Services Department)

Abstract:

Aims: To review the registration procedures for visually impaired people, and to assess service provision, within the County of Avon.

Methods: Major source of information questionnaires and personal interviews with staff of Avon SSD. Comparison of service delivery model with four other local authorities. Analysis related to recent reports and legislation concerning visually impaired people and/or disabled people in general.

Current status: Completed.

Summary of findings:

Profile of services in Avon at time of report shows absence of common policy and standards of service delivery beyond the statutory responsibility for registration.

Comparative examination of models of service delivery in Avon and four other local authorities; comments linked to *A Wider Vision* (SSI, 1988b), Chronically Sick and Disabled Persons Act 1970, and Disabled Persons (Service, Consultation and Representation) Act 1986.

Identifies six sub-groups of visually impaired people who require specialist services.

Recommendations: Thirteen, including need to: review existing services; develop a specialist team or teams with appropriate County-wide management support; and review co-ordination of services with voluntary sector and other statutory services.

Subjects of study: Visually impaired people in Avon, including registered blind and partially sighted people: all ages and conditions.

Coverage: Focus on County of Avon, but note approach involved comparative review of four other local authorities and reference to national reports and legislation.

Timescale: 1 March 1988 - 31 July 1988.
20 researcher weeks.

Cost:

Funding body/bodies: Study undertaken whilst holding a Personal Social Services Fellowship at the University of Bristol, on secondment from post as Team Manager, Avon SSD.

Report(s): Report published by and available from Bristol Royal Society for the Blind. Price £2.50p.

SERVICES FOR PEOPLE WITH DISABILITIES

Researcher(s): Joanna Wilkin, Sue Wilson, Andrea
Ruddock-West, Christine Morgan,
Dave Walton (Evaluation Project Team)
Social Services Department
Westminster City Council
PO Box 240, City Hall
Victoria Street, London SW1E 6QP
Tel: 0171 828 8070

Abstract:

Aims: Examination and review of services for people with disabilities, including those with a visual impairment, in the light of the implications of the 1986 Disabled Persons Act, changes in the organization of the Social Services Department, Health Districts and Housing Department, and the development of the policy of 'community care'. Examination to include criteria for provision of services and views on new structure.

Methods: Analysis of existing information within the Department; interviews with members of staff; requests for written evidence. Same procedure with key agencies. Case studies. Snapshot survey of one week's referrals for occupational therapy, domiciliary and social work services. Small survey and open forum consultation with small group of disabled people and their carers.

Current status: Completed.

Summary of findings:

Visually impaired people: Less services available in 1987 for this client group than in 1983 when a Planning Group made recommendations. Urgent need to recruit specialist workers - unreasonable to think that non-specialist generic teams can meet relevant needs adequately. Also need to provide better information to this client group - procedure manual last updated 1977.

General: Disabled people are the SSD's largest client group and numbers are increasing. Lack of planning, leading to wastage of resources. Services are fragmented. Staff show a high level of commitment, but perceive work with disabled people as having a low status.

Subjects of study: All disabled people known to the local authority, plus relevant staff and agencies.

Coverage: City of Westminster.

Timescale: November 1986 - February 1987.

Cost:

Funding body/bodies: 'In-house' project.

Report(s):   February 1987. Internal to Department, but obtainable on request from Westminster Social Services Department.

'SERVICES FOR PEOPLE WITH A VISUAL IMPAIRMENT: A REPORT ON CURRENT SERVICES AVAILABLE TO PEOPLE WITH A VISUAL IMPAIRMENT IN SOUTH DEVON AND RECOMMENDATIONS FOR THEIR FUTURE DEVELOPMENT'

Researcher(s):   John Collins
                  Partially Sighted Society
                  Sight Centre, Dean Clarke House
                  Southernhay East
                  Exeter, Devon EX1 1PE
                  Tel: 01392 210656

                  (for the South Devon Review and Planning Group)

Abstract:

A study of current service delivery systems, identifying gaps and proposing an alternative, comprehensive rehabilitation service. Part of a wider study commissioned by the South Devon Review and Planning Group into the needs of people suffering a sensory loss. Two other groups studied were those with a hearing loss and those with a dual sensory loss. Information here only concerns those with a visual impairment.

Aims: Identification of client group aged 16-65. Identification of needs, attitudes and service requirements. Review of current services. Identification of deficiencies in services. Preparation of report.

Methods: Epidemiological predictions and comparative analysis of local and national data. Identification of sources of services in local area, nature of services, and patterns of delivery, including voluntary sector.

Current status: Completed.

Summary of findings:

Services inconsistent in terms of standards and unco-ordinated. 'The main problem is that the responsibility for providing rehabilitation services generally lies with local social services departments, whilst the diagnosis of the visual impairment itself is the responsibility of health authorities'.

Recommendations: General: an 'inter-disciplinary approach' is necessary, where different professionals are regarded as being equally important and as carrying equal responsibility in relation to 'the overall objective of minimising the disabling effect of the impairment'.

To specific problems identified: appropriate and full assessment; counselling; and provision of low vision assessment and training.

Subjects of study: People with a significant and permanent visual impairment, whether registered or not.

Coverage:

Timescale: March - June 1990.

Cost:

Funding body/bodies:

Report(s): June 1990. Title as at top of entry. General availability.

VISUALLY DISABLED SERVICES IN TAMESIDE: REPORT BY RNIB CONSULTANCY SERVICE

Researcher(s): Alan Bunting
Principal Officer (Research)
Social Services Department
Tameside Metropolitan Borough Council
Council Offices, Wellington Road
Ashton-under-Lyne
Tameside OL6 6DL
Tel: 0161 330 8355 x 3352

RNIB Consultancy Service
Royal National Institute for the Blind
224 Great Portland Street
London W1N 6AA
Tel: 0171 388 1266

Abstract:

Independent report commissioned by the Director of Social Services.

Aims: To provide an assessment of the availability, quality and effectiveness of services to visually impaired people within the Borough, and to provide advice for the future development of these services.

Methods: A service audit of the Sensory Handicap Team (newly-established in 1987). A survey of fieldwork teams working with elderly people. A survey of residential and day care services, with a brief consumer survey. A survey of service inputs from other voluntary or statutory services.

Current status: Completed.

Summary of findings:

Findings and recommendations reflect the broad themes concerning service needs and development identified in *Local Authority Social Rehabilitation Services to Visually Handicapped People* (Shore, 1985) and *A Wider Vision* (SSI,

1988b).

Subjects of study: See Abstract.

Coverage: Metropolitan Borough of Tameside.

Timescale: November 1987 - November 1989.

Cost:

Funding body/bodies:

Report(s):   Available only by permission of the Director of Social Services.

'WORKING TOGETHER: THE SCOPE FOR IMPROVING WORKING LINKS BETWEEN RNIB AND LOCAL SOCIETIES FOR THE BLIND'

Researcher(s): Graham Lomas and Hywel Vaughan
Royal National Institute for the Blind
224 Great Portland Street
London W1N 6AA
Tel: 0171 388 1266

Abstract:

Part of a wider development programme initiated by the RNIB to improve its services. The report, *Working Together*, examines relationship between RNIB and local societies for the blind. The work in this review was integrated with a concurrent analysis of fund raising agreements between the RNIB and local voluntary organizations.

Aims: 'The main purpose ... was to understand how the societies work, what their plans are, what help the RNIB can be, and what factors the organization (i.e. RNIB) should take into account regarding local societies in its own major development programmes.'

Methods: Sample of forty-six local societies, reflecting regional balance, range of activities and services, sources of funding, urban and rural conditions, and history and general scale of the organization. Use of structured report schedules, interviews with employed and voluntary officers. Informal discussions. Analysis of links with a number of local social services departments. Discussions with six national charities that have working links with the local groups. Discussions with the secretaries of the Regional Associations in England and the Scottish National Federation for the Blind. Varying degrees of formal contact with a small number of consumer groups.

Current status: Completed.

Summary of findings:

There is no standard model of a local voluntary organization for visually impaired people. Local societies are primarily concerned with the care of elderly people. They rarely cater for or attract younger people with visual impairments. (RNIB client services cover all ages.) Little evidence of joint planning or partnerships of equals between the local societies and the relevant social services department(s). Lack of clarification of roles and responsibilities. Low level of working knowledge of the work of the RNIB among local societies, beyond equipment and talking books. Local societies do not have a clear idea of their own existing or future potential.

Recommendations: Twenty-six, including: develop resource centres, possibly linked with rehabilitation services at regional, area and local level; improve information services, especially to local society officers; improve national image and national awareness of RNIB.

Subjects of study:

Coverage:

Timescale: 1985 - January 1986.

Cost:

Funding body/bodies:

Report(s):   Lomas, G. and Vaughan, H. (1987), *Working Together: The Scope for Improving Working Links between RNIB and Local Societies for the Blind,* RNIB, London.

ASPECTS OF DISABILITY

Researcher(s):   Social Services Department,
Humberside County Council
Brunswick House, Strand Close
Beverley Road
Hull, North Humberside HU2 9DB
Tel: 01482 867131

Abstract:

A strategy for physically disabled and sensory impaired people is currently being developed across Humberside County Council. The strategy is to be based on both local and national research.

Methods: Several task groups are periodically reporting to the Social Services Committee. The task groups cover services, employment, leisure, etc., for people aged up to sixty-five years. The groups include people with sensory impairments working alongside social services staff.

Current status: In progress.

Summary of findings:

Subjects of study: Disabled people below the age of sixty-five.

Coverage: County of Humberside.

Timescale: October 1989 - March 1990.

Cost:

Funding body/bodies: 'In-house' project.

Report(s):   Not a public document until it has been to Social Services Committee.

REVIEW OF SERVICES FOR PEOPLE WITH A VISUAL DISABILITY

Researcher(s): Carol Cooknell
Senior Practitioner (Physical Disability)
Social Services Department
Buckinghamshire County Council
Easton Street
High Wycombe, Bucks HP11 1NH
Tel: 01494 475239

Abstract:

Aims: To improve services for blind and/or partially sighted people, whether registered or not. To review social services provision in light of the SSI report *A Wider Vision* (1988b) and the Department of Health report *Co-ordinating Services for Visually Handicapped People* (1989b). Particular concern to consider the relevance, accessibility and co-ordination of services provided by SSD and their integration with those provided by a range of other departments and organizations.

Methods: A variety of mechanisms have been adopted to seek information and views from a range of individuals and interested groups. These include: announcements in local newspapers, on local radio and in 'talking newspapers', informing people of the review and inviting comment; meetings with workers of Buckinghamshire Association for the Blind in various parts of the County; staff questionnaire; targeted approaches to Joint Advisory Groups with Health Authority, District Councils and voluntary organizations. There may also be meetings with consultant ophthalmologists.

Current status: Completion anticipated 31 March 1990. Report to Social Services Committee anticipated June 1990.

Summary of findings:

Subjects of study:

Coverage: County of Buckinghamshire.

Timescale: 1 August 1989 - 31 March 1990.

Cost: £4,000 (approx.) in terms of staff time, travelling expenses, publicity material, and cost of publishing final report.

Funding body/bodies: 'In-house' project.

Report(s):   For discussion by Social Services Committee in June 1990.   General availability thereafter if approved.

STRATEGIC FRAMEWORK 1991 - 2001

Researcher(s):   V. Poad
Bedfordshire Joint Care Planning Team
Social Services Department
County Hall, Cauldwell Street
Bedford MK42 9AP
Tel: 01234 363222 x 2361

Abstract:

A comprehensive strategy to guide services for people who are blind or partially sighted. Planning group will include Social Services, Health, FPC, Education, Housing, voluntary sector and users.

Methods: Literature search; review of current practices; user survey.

Current status: Planning.

Summary of findings:

Subjects of study: Blind and partially sighted people.

Coverage: County of Bedfordshire.

Timescale: 1 April 1990 - 1 October 1990.

Cost:

Funding body/bodies: Part of normal duties.

Report(s):

'THE CLIENTS' VIEW: SOCIAL AND REHABILITATION SERVICES FOR VISUALLY DISABLED PEOPLE - ARE THEY MEETING THE NEED?'

Researcher(s): John Collins
Partially Sighted Society
Sight Centre, Dean Clarke House
Southernay East
Exeter, Devon EX1 1PE
Tel: 01392 210656

Abstract:

Aims: To identify the range of services currently being provided for visually impaired people by the statutory and voluntary agencies within the six counties making up the South West of England. To investigate how far vision enhancement services have permeated through to current service providers. To ascertain whether current services meet the expressed needs of those receiving them. To identify gaps in current service provision which could be met by a voluntary agency.

Methods: The original intention was to administer a questionnaire to twenty-five registered blind or partially sighted people in each county, in face-to-face interviews. Permission was refused by all but Avon, on grounds of confidentiality, administrative or staffing problems. A compromise was reached with the other five authorities by sending a postal questionnaire to potential respondents. A questionnaire was also sent to all six LAs and to relevant local voluntary organizations, to identify the services they offered and to compare with those which the respondents received.

Current status: Completed.

Summary of findings:

No significant difference in the quality or quantity of service provision in the five counties studied. No significant difference in the levels of satisfaction stated by respondents in the various counties. Levels of satisfaction appeared to vary between individual services rather than between areas.

The most common criticism was 'lack of information on what services are available'. Vision substitution services were offered more frequently than services for vision enhancement. Services to help visually impaired people make full use of lighting, colour contrast and low vision aids and equipment were most inadequate. Lack of counselling services and help with securing or maintaining employment. More respondents stated a higher level of satisfaction with special residential education than with special day schools/units or mainstream education.

Subjects of study:	81 respondents; aged 12-88 years; 46 male, 35 female; 54 blind, 27 partially sighted. 42 took part in face-to-face interviews; 39 completed postal questionnaires.
Coverage:	See Abstract and Subjects of study.
Timescale:	Autumn 1985 - 1986.
Cost:	
Funding body/bodies:	
Report(s):	A report, an abridged version of Collins' final CQSW course project (title as at top of entry), is available from the Partially Sighted Society. Price £5.00p.

TRANSPORT FACILITIES FOR THE VISUALLY IMPAIRED IN BRISTOL

Researcher(s):   R.J.R. Hitchings
                   c/o Bristol Royal Society for the Blind
                   Stillhouse Lane
                   Bedminster, Bristol BS3 4EB
                   Tel: 0117 953 7750

Abstract:

Aims: To establish the exact needs of visually impaired people in regard to transport, and to determine workable solutions.

Methods: Questionnaires and personal interviews.

Current status: Complete. Open seminar on transport held in January 1990. Ongoing monitoring and review.

Summary of findings:

Detailed report on the transport problems encountered specifically by visually impaired people in the area served by the BRSB. Accessibility, availability, reliability and comfort of public transport posed difficulties for some people. Mini-buses were not found comfortable for long journeys. Taxis were found to be expensive and not always reliable. Relying on volunteers, friends and family created an unacceptable level of dependency. Mobility of clients was also affected by health problems additional to visual impairment. Sixty per cent said they would go out more if they could improve their transport arrangements.

Recommendations: Relate specifically to the groups and area served by BRSB, but could provide models applicable elsewhere.

Subjects of study:	Visually impaired people in Bristol: registered blind and partially sighted, all ages and conditions.
Coverage:	See above.
Timescale:	1 February 1989 - 30 October 1989.
Cost:	£800 (approx.).
Funding body/bodies:	Bristol Royal Society for the Blind.
Report(s):	Available from the Society.

VISUALLY HANDICAPPED PEOPLE IN HAMPSHIRE: A SURVEY OF NEEDS

Researcher(s): Sally Edge
c/o Sight Concern Hampshire, Hampshire Association
   for the Care of the Blind
25 Church Road, Bishopstoke
Eastleigh, Hampshire SO50 6BL
Tel: 01703 641244

Abstract:

Survey to discover the needs of all visually impaired people in Hampshire, excluding Portsmouth. (Portsmouth Voluntary Association elected to conduct interviews in their own catchment area using slightly different methods; their results were not included in this report.) Topics covered included accommodation, registration status, causes of sight loss, contact with ophthalmologist, other health problems, communication skills, mobility, daily living skills, specialized aids used, contact with Hampshire Social Services Department, contact with voluntary organizations, and analysis of special sub-groups.

Methods: Questionnaire administered by fifteen interviewers recruited and trained for the project. Discussions with various members of staff in the relevant agencies.

Current status: Completed.

Summary of findings:

50 per cent of respondents registered blind, 34 per cent partially sighted, 9 per cent not registered, 7 per cent did not know their registration status. Majority of respondents female, over retirement age, with 1 or more additional health problems and living alone. 17 per cent of total number interviewed lived in residential homes and 2.5 per cent lived permanently in hospital. 75 per cent had substantially or entirely lost ability to read or write, but few using alternative communication techniques. Mobility: heavy dependence on sighted guides. Symbol cane most used specialist aid. Other mobility aids indicated other health problems: e.g. Zimmer

frames. Daily living skills: little difference found between the sexes - female relatives were the most frequently identified carers, followed by staff in homes and home helps. Contact with SSD mainly very low. Talking books most popular voluntary service.

Recommendations: Increase and standardize provision of specialist SSD staff throughout the County. Voluntary organizations can increase and standardize their roles. Health and other services need to be more aware of the needs of visually impaired people and incorporate them into the development of their services.

Subjects of study:	All known registered blind and partially sighted people in Hampshire (excluding Portsmouth), including those in residential homes and hospitals. Survey participants also included some with a severe sight loss who had not been registered. 4,796 visually impaired people were contacted and 3,200 interviewed.
Coverage:	County of Hampshire, excluding City of Portsmouth.
Timescale:	July 1984 - August 1985.
Cost:	
Funding body/bodies:	Part-time salary for Project Supervisor: MSC to August 1985; Hampshire SSD September 1985 - December 1986.
Report(s):	Report completed December 1986 (published 1987). Available from HACB. Price £3.50p.

THE ELDERS PROJECT: A LONGITUDINAL ENQUIRY

Researcher(s):   Michael J. Tobin and Eileen W. Hill
Research Centre for the Education of the Visually
Handicapped, School of Education
University of Birmingham, Edgbaston
Birmingham B15 2TT
Tel: 0121 414 6737

Abstract:

This project is concerned with the skills and needs of visually impaired people aged sixty years and above. Among the specific themes being investigated are possible differences between people with a congenital visual impairment and those whose impairment is of later onset, in terms of various coping strategies and perceptual and cognitive abilities (with a focus upon whether and how these abilities change over time).

Methods: A variety of methods to assess skills and needs in relation to sight loss: psychometric testing; interviews (structured and unstructured) to elicit information about needs and methods of coping. All subjects are to be tested/interviewed on a regular basis (twice yearly as a minimum).

Current status: Data collection in process.

Summary of findings:

Subjects of study: People registered as blind or partially sighted, and aged sixty and above.

Coverage: Sample of local visually impaired people.

Timescale: Began 1 January 1989.

Cost: £7,500 per annum (present estimate). (Excludes Project Director's time - paid for by the University of Birmingham.)

Funding body/bodies: At present, funding is from RNIB, Birmingham Royal Institution for the Blind, and the charity Blindness: Research for Learning, Work and Leisure.

Report(s):   Preliminary report will be submitted for publication by end of Summer 1990.

GENERAL NEEDS SURVEY

Researcher(s):   Prof. Aubrey C. McKennell and Errol C. Walker
c/o Royal National Institute for the Blind
224 Great Portland Street
London W1N 6AA
Tel: 0171 388 1266

Abstract:

Aims: To provide information which will enable the RNIB to evaluate, promote and develop its services. To identify problems in obtaining information about services or access to them. To provide a national picture of the characteristics of the visually impaired population. To examine how the needs of the visually impaired population are being met from whatever source, including other service providers. To give evidence of significant areas of unmet or inadequately met need, so that the RNIB or other agencies can take steps to ensure that those needs are met. To identify areas for further investigation. To extend and complement the information on the severely visually impaired gathered in the *OPCS Disability Surveys* (1988 and 1989).

Methods: Nationwide sample survey drawn from visually impaired respondents to the *OPCS Disability Surveys*. 600 home interviews, using a questionnaire on social characteristics and nineteen areas of need.

Current status: Finalizing Adult Report. Analysis of Children's Study commenced.

Summary of findings:

Subjects of study:	600 visually impaired people who took part in the *OPCS Disability Surveys*: 200 aged 60 yrs and over, 200 between 16 and 59 yrs, 200 children - interviewing parents where appropriate.
Coverage:	National sample of 600 people drawn from *OPCS Disability Surveys*.
Timescale:	1984 - 1991.
Cost:	
Funding body/bodies:	
Report(s):	Adults - scheduled January 1991.
	Children - scheduled Spring 1992.

PREVENTION OF BLINDNESS: AN EXAMINATION OF CHANGING PATTERNS OF CARE AND THE IMPACT ON SIGHT LOSS

Researcher(s):   Dr C.J. Burns-Cox
c/o Bristol Royal Society for the Blind
Stillhouse Lane
Bedminster, Bristol BS3 4EB
Tel: 0117 953 7750

Abstract:

Examining changing patterns of care and the impact on sight loss. Contact Dr Burns-Cox for further details.

Methods: Collating information from BD8 forms.

Current status: Ongoing.

Summary of findings:

Subjects of study:

Coverage:

Timescale: Commenced January 1990; study expanding.

Cost:

Funding body/bodies:

Reports):

SURVEY AND REVIEW OF NEEDS

Researcher(s): Social Services Division
Department of Social Services and Housing
London Borough of Bromley
The Walnuts, High Street
Orpington, Kent BR6 0UN
Tel: 01869 8369009

(in association with Kent Association for the Blind
72 College Road, Maidstone, Kent ME15 6SJ
Tel: 01622 691357)

Abstract:

An analysis of residents within the Borough of Bromley. This will be used to negotiate a brief with Kent Association for the Blind to act as agents in providing fieldwork services for visually impaired people.

Methods: Interviews.

Current status:

Summary of findings:

Subjects of study: Registered blind and partially sighted people, aged over sixty.

Coverage: Orpington, London Borough of Bromley.

Timescale: Commenced September 1989. Estimated completion by end June 1990.

Cost:

Funding body/bodies: Partly funded by London Borough of Bromley.

Report(s):

SURVEY OF NEEDS: VISUALLY IMPAIRED PEOPLE
OF CAMBRIDGESHIRE

Researcher(s):   Cambridgeshire Society for the Blind and Partially
         Sighted
         East View, 5 Coles Lane
         Oakington, Cambridge CB4 5BA
         Tel: 01223 236868

Abstract:

Aims: To establish the needs of visually impaired people. To provide a profile of statistics for the County. To raise the profile of the Society so as to uncover blind and partially sighted people previously unknown to ourselves and Social Services.

Methods: A survey in Cambridge City and surrounding villages in the old County of Cambridge, carried out by specially recruited and trained volunteers.

Current status: Several villages completed, including some analysis.
         RNIB social scientists to review methodology. Computer
         analysis will be used in future.

Summary of findings:

Subjects of study: Blind and partially sighted people, whether registered or not.

Coverage: Cambridge City and surrounding villages in the old County of Cambridge.

Timescale: September 1988 - June 1991.
19 researcher weeks.

Cost:

Funding body/bodies: DHSS; RNIB; Opportunities for Volunteers.

Report(s):

SURVEY OF NEEDS OF VISUALLY IMPAIRED PEOPLE WITHIN THE TEN DISTRICTS COVERED BY THE CHESTER BLIND WELFARE SOCIETY

Researcher(s):   Mrs A.P. Walker
Chester Blind Welfare Society
67 Liverpool Road
Chester CH2 1AP
Tel: 01244 382222

Abstract:

Aims: To explore whether the individual with a visual impairment is satisfied with the services provided, and whether the services have aided independence. The survey offers individuals the opportunity to contribute to discussions between those who use the services and those who provide services.

Methods: Questionnaire in large print. Mainly closed questions, due to visual impairment of respondents. Two final open-ended questions for comments.

Current status: Analysis under way and report being written.

Summary of findings:

Subjects of study:	1,500 registered blind and partially sighted people known to the Society.
Coverage:	Cheshire: Chester, Ellesmere Port, Runcorn, Knutsford, Nantwich and Crewe, Congleton, Vale Royal.
	Clwyd: Alyn Deeside, Delyn, Rhuddlan.
Timescale:	May 1989 - March 1990.
Cost:	£1,000.
Funding body/bodies:	Cecilia Trust.
Report(s):	Available to Clwyd and Cheshire local authority managers and rehabilitation officers, plus other interested parties.

'OPERATION CATARACT': OPERATIONS ON A DAY CARE BASIS WITH HOTEL AFTER-CARE

Researcher(s):   Mrs C.E. Hicks
Director, Impact Foundation
Worthing District Health Authority
Westview House, Westview
Lindfield, West Sussex RH16 2LJ
Tel: 01444 483439

(Impact Foundation also 01444 457080)

Abstract:

Modern surgical techniques lend themselves to high turnover; this has outpaced available hospital bed capacity. An experiment to see whether cataract operations could be offered to visually impaired people as day patients, with post-operative supervision and care provided in hotel accommodation instead of hospital beds.

Planning and liaison between Impact Foundation, Worthing District Health Authority, staff at the Berkeley Hotel Worthing, and voluntary organizations. 100 patients who had been waiting the longest for cataract operations were selected from local NHS waiting list. Medical and nursing staff were made available for pre-operative care at the hotel; operation under local anaesthetic at the hospital; post-operative care for up to five nights at the hotel. Hotel staff provided normal domestic care; volunteers undertook reception and clerical duties and transport.

Current status: Completed.

Summary of findings:

Independent medical assessment and follow-up showed professional standards not compromised by post-operative care in hotel. No difficulties in providing nursing services in hotel setting; duties done by volunteers and hotel staff gave nurses more time with patients. Patients took more responsibility for self-care and independence than in hospital.

Voluntary organizations: WRVS did clerical and reception duties; Red Cross and Rotary organized transport; local church and other organizations organized a service and entertainment; financial contributions made by a variety of local and national organizations, which all appear satisfied with their roles.

Patient survey showed a high level of satisfaction with medical and nursing care in hospital and hotel. Patients enjoyed the independence of post-operative care in the hotel.

Costs: £431 per patient (NHS inpatient £680; private bed £1,500).

Subjects of study: 100 patients awaiting cataract operations. Over 80 per cent were over 65 years of age.

Coverage: Worthing District Health Authority.

Timescale: May - December 1987.

Cost: £43,125.

Funding body/bodies: £17,062 contributed by voluntary resources.

Report(s):

EVALUATION STUDY OF AN ADVISER/COUNSELLOR BASED AT AN EYE HOSPITAL

Researcher(s): Brighton Society for the Blind
Linkway Lodge, The Linkway
Hollingford, Brighton BN1 7EJ
Tel: 01273 507251

Abstract:

Volunteer advisers/counsellors based at an eye hospital, supervised by a paid worker, to offer help and to observe the need for specific help to newly registered blind and partially sighted people.

Methods: Monitoring and evaluation over one year. Information to be collected regarding specific help offered and uptake, numbers helped, benefits to patients, age groups involved.

Current status: Planning for start of project.

Summary of findings:

Subjects of study:	Patients, regardless of age or registration status.
Coverage:	Hospital catchment area.
Timescale:	14 May 1990 - 14 May 1991.
Cost:	
Funding body/bodies:	'In-house' project. Volunteers' expenses paid by Society; administrative costs by Opportunities for Volunteers and RNIB.
Report(s):	

THE DEVELOPMENT OF MEASURES OF LOW VISION MOBILITY PERFORMANCE

Researcher(s): Dr Allan G. Dodds
Blind Mobility Research Unit
Department of Psychology
University of Nottingham
University Park, Nottingham NG7 2RD
Tel: 0115 951 5315

Denis P. Davis (p-t postgraduate student)
RNIB Employment Rehabilitation Centre
Manor House, Middle Lincombe Road
Torquay, Devon TQ1 2NG
Tel: 01803 214523

Abstract:

Aims: To develop objective measures of low vision mobility performance.

Methods: Video analysis of mobility.

Current status: Completed.

Summary of findings:

Two new measures developed: proportion of correction detections (PCD) and preview. Together with preferred walking speed (PWS), these measures enable distinction between performance of clients who are given low vision training and those who are not.

Subjects of study:	Partially sighted clients.

Coverage:

Timescale:	1 January 1985 - 31 December 1988.

Cost:	£7,691.

Funding body/bodies:	Part of core programme.

Report(s):   Dodds, A.G. and Davis, D.P. (1987), 'Low vision assessment and training for mobility', *International Journal of Rehabilitation Research*, vol. 10, no. 3, pp. 327-30.

Dodds, A.G. and Davis, D.P. (1988), 'Low vision: functional assessment and training', in Neustadt-Noy, N., Merin, S. and Schiff, Y. (eds), *Orientation and Mobility of the Visually Impaired* (Proc. of Fourth International Mobility Conference, held May 1986, Jerusalem), Heiliger, Jerusalem, pp. 29-34.

Dodds, A.G. and Davis, D.P. (1989), 'Assessment and training of low vision clients for mobility', *Journal of Visual Impairment & Blindness*, vol. 83, no. 9, pp. 439-46.

EVALUATION OF TASK LIGHTING

Researcher(s):   John Collins
Partially Sighted Society
Sight Centre, Dean Clarke House
Southernhay East
Exeter, Devon EX1 1PE
Tel: 01392 210656

Abstract:

Part of the Partially Sighted Society's Low Vision Services Project, at the National Low Vision Advice Centre, Exeter.

Aims: To identify whether visually impaired people could improve their near vision task performance by using specific lighting units.

Methods: Objective and subjective evaluation.

Current status: Completed.

Summary of findings:

Experiment sought to establish which kind of light bulb is both objectively and subjectively best for enhancing the vision of partially sighted people. Fluorescent and daylight blue bulbs were perceived and demonstrated as more successful for reading print from a Keeler 'A' chart than the 60 watt Opal Tidylite, but it was not possible to test for colour. A disadvantage with the daylight blue bulbs is that they lose light through the blue glass and therefore 100 watt bulbs are required, making close work for a prolonged period very hot.

Subjects of study:	Sixty registered blind or partially sighted people, aged 14-84 years, suffering from a variety of common eye disorders.
Coverage:	Local sample.
Timescale:	January 1987 - March 1987.
Cost:	£500.
Funding body/bodies:	'In-house' study.
Report(s):	*The evaluation of three types of light source for near vision tasks*, by John Collins, National Low Vision Training Officer, The Partially Sighted Society, March 1987.

LOW VISION SERVICES IN AVON

c/o Bristol Royal Society for the Blind
Stillhouse Lane
Bedminster, Bristol BS3 4EB
Tel: 0117 953 7750

Aims: To examine the present level of services in regard to low vision, and to recommend a new structure for a multidisciplinary approach.

Methods: To be established.

Current status: Planning and initial data collection in progress.

Summary of findings:

Subjects of study: Registered blind and partially sighted people who will benefit from a low vision service.

Coverage:

Timescale: Commenced 1 December 1989.

Cost: Not yet established.

Funding body/bodies:

Report(s):

MOTION VISION IN THE PARTIALLY SIGHTED

Researcher(s):   Dr Anthony J. Doyle and Ms Michelle D. Lee
Blind Mobility Research Unit
Department of Psychology
University of Nottingham
University Park, Nottingham NG7 2RD
Tel: 0115 951 5315

Abstract:

There is some evidence to suggest that more than five per cent of the population has difficulty interpreting pure motion clues. Little is known about normative behaviour in this field and it is a distinct possibility that people with defective central vision may be more heavily dependent on motion processing than those with normal sight, which can to some extent be used to provide alternative means of obtaining motion information when it is not available from more direct sources. A computer based testing procedure is being developed, to test subjects in exclusively motion clues both in the foveal area and in the periphery. Quite apart from highlighting the sort of performance and defects which bear specifically on mobility tasks, there is also the possibility that training in computer displayed motion tasks might assist partially sighted people to improve their abilities in this respect.

Methods: The test is being written for the IBM and IBM-compatible micros in the 'C' language, so that it may be used on a standard machine by anyone with a smattering of computer ability. In this way it should be possible to gather data on partially sighted subjects at remote sites by sending them a disc copy. This procedure was shown to be workable with the BMRU's 'Ocula' system.

Current status: All the more difficult computer problems have now been solved and the formal construction of the presentation and scoring parts of the test are under way.

Summary of findings:

Subjects of study: The bulk of the normative data will come from undergraduates or sixth form school children. The test will also be administered to as many partially sighted people as possible.

Coverage: See Subjects of study.

Timescale: January 1990 - Summer 1991 (est.).

Cost: £21,840.

Funding body/bodies: Part of core programme.

Report(s):

GAIT ANALYSIS

Researcher(s): Dr David D. Clark-Carter
c/o Blind Mobility Research Unit
Department of Psychology
University of Nottingham
University Park, Nottingham NG7 2RD
Tel: 0115 951 5315

(subsequently Staffordshire University
Tel: 01782 744531)

Abstract:

Aims: To develop a means of determining moment-to-moment walking speed.

Methods: Laboratory and field.

Current status: Completed.

Summary of findings:

Blind people have a preferred walking speed (PWS). Their adopted walking speed (AWS) when using a mobility aid is always less than their PWS. A measure known as PPWS (percentage of preferred walking speed - the AWS/PWS ratio) enables measurement of changes in gait as a function of aid provision or training.

Subjects of study:	Totally blind people.
Coverage:	
Timescale:	1 January 1984 - 31 December 1987.
Cost:	£60,000.
Funding body/bodies:	Part of core programme.
Report(s):	Clark-Carter, D.D, (1985), *Factors affecting blind mobility*, PhD Thesis, University of Nottingham.
	Clark-Carter, D.D., Heyes, A.D. and Howarth, C.I. (1986), 'The effect of non-visual preview upon the walking speed of visually impaired people', *Ergonomics*, vol. 29, no. 12, pp. 1575-81.
	Clark-Carter, D.D., Heyes, A.D. and Howarth, C.I. (1987), 'The gait of visually impaired pedestrians' (Research Note), *Human Movement Science*, vol. 6, pp. 277-82.

INVESTIGATION OF MOBILITY RELATED FEELINGS

Researcher(s):   Dr W.D. Alan Beggs
Blind Mobility Research Unit
Department of Psychology
University of Nottingham
University Park, Nottingham NG7 2RD
Tel: 0115 951 5315

Abstract:

Little is known about the emotional correlates of visually impaired travel, apart from its stressful nature and the tendency of travellers to be under-motivated to use the mobility skills which they are taught by mobility officers. It was decided to investigate the feelings associated with travel, with a view to gaining a practical and theoretical understanding of these emotional processes.

Methods: A three phase method was used. Initially, depth interviews yielded a qualitative understanding of the breadth of such feelings. A second phase then identified specific words which totally blind and partially sighted travellers would themselves use to describe their feelings on a journey. From these, a twenty-one item questionnaire was developed. Finally, the structure of this semantic space was investigated by means of a factor analysis of the responses of a large sample of clients who completed the questionnaire after a short journey.

Current status: Completed.

Summary of findings:

Three orthogonal factors accounted for over eighty-three per cent of the common variance. The largest was termed 'self-efficacy', and included words associated with the perceived threat of travel, perceived competency to meet that threat, and the associated emotional distress of anxiety and loss in confidence. Bandura's self-efficacy theory is a useful theoretical description of the processes underlying emotional distress. The second factor was termed 'cognitive arousal', and contained words relating to the problem solving and information processing demands of travel. The third and smallest factor was termed 'role acceptance', and was concerned with the embarrassment of being seen to be a cane user. The questionnaire will be used further, to track changes in feelings that occur as visually impaired clients are taught to become mobile again, and to evaluate the effectiveness of different interventions.

Subjects of study: Seventy-one clients were involved, varying in degree of sight loss from totally blind to partially sighted.

Coverage:

Timescale: January 1986 - December 1988.
50 researcher weeks.

Cost: £25,332.

Funding body/bodies: Part of core programme.

Report(s): *Report to the Chief Scientist, Research Management Division, Department of Health & Social Security, covering the period 1 April 1984 to 31 March 1988, including future proposals*, July 1988, pp. 40-5.

Beggs, W.D.A., 'The emotional correlates of visually impaired mobility', paper submitted (10 April 1990) to *Journal of Visual Impairment & Blindness*.

THE 'SONIC PATHFINDER'

Researcher(s):   Dr Anthony D. Heyes
c/o Blind Mobility Research Unit
Department of Psychology
University of Nottingham
University Park, Nottingham NG7 2RD
Tel: 0115 951 5315

(subsequently in Australia)

Abstract:

Aims: To develop an ultra-sonic, spectacle-mounted mobility aid.

Methods: Laboratory development with field evaluation.

Current status: Completed.

Summary of findings:

A head-mounted ultrasonic mobility aid has been developed and evaluated. The inventor is currently in the process of producing a commercially available version.

Subjects of study:	Totally blind people.
Coverage:	
Timescale:	1 January 1980 - 31 December 1987. 350 researcher weeks (est.).
Cost:	£173,000.
Funding body/bodies:	
Report(s):	Heyes, A.D. (1984), 'A new electronic travel aid', *Journal of Visual Impairment & Blindness*, vol. 78, no. 5, pp. 200-2.
	Heyes, A.D. (1984), 'Sonic Pathfinder: a programmable guidance aid for the blind', *Electronics & Wireless World*, vol. 90, no. 1579, April, pp. 26-9 & p. 62.
	Heyes, A.D. (1986), 'Whatever happened to the Sonic Pathfinder?' (Letter), *Electronic & Wireless World*, April, p. 38.
	Dodds, A.G., Clark-Carter, D.D. and Howarth C.I. (1984), 'The Sonic Pathfinder: an evaluation', *Journal of Visual Impairment & Blindness*, vol. 78, no. 5, pp. 203-6.
	Dodds, A.G. (1985), 'Evaluating mobility aids - an evolving methodology', in Warren, D.H. and Strelow, E.R. (eds), *Electronic Spatial Sensing for the Blind*, Martinus Nijhoff, The Hague, pp. 191-200.

SPATIAL REPRESENTATION AND CONGENITAL BLINDNESS

Researcher(s):   Dr Allan G. Dodds and Ms Michelle D. Lee
Blind Mobility Research Unit
Department of Psychology
University of Nottingham
University Park, Nottingham NG7 2RD
Tel: 0115 951 5315

Ms Deborah J. Hellawell
(subsequently University of Durham
Tel: 0191 374 2000)

Abstract:

Teachers of blind children have subscribed to the view that congenital blindness caused by retrolental fibroplasia (RLF) produces deficits in spatial understanding. The work described tests this hypothesis.

Methods: Experiment involving two groups, each of twenty subjects (one RLF; one non-RLF) were presented with an orientation task after having been matched on a number of IQ sub-tasks. The dependent variable was angular error on a pointing task.

Current status: Completed.

Summary of findings:

No differences were observed between groups, thus refuting the hypothesis. A highly significant correlation between performance on a similarities task and angular error in the orientation task suggested that early experience contributes to later spatial understanding.

Subjects of study: Two sample groups of registered blind children, as indicated in Abstract.

Coverage:

Timescale: 1 September 1988 - 30 June 1989.
50 researcher weeks.

Cost: £12,500.

Funding body/bodies: Part of core programme.

Report(s):   Dodds, A.G. (1989), 'Tactile maps and the blind user: perceptual, cognitive and behavioural factors', in Tatham, A.F. and Dodds, A.G. (eds), *Proceedings of the 2nd International Symposium on Maps and Graphics for Visually Handicapped People*, University of Nottingham.

Dodds, A.G. (1989), 'Tactile maps: a psychologist's perspective', *Cartographic Journal*, vol. 26, pp. 3-6.

Dodds, A.G., Hellawell, D.J. and Lee, M.D., 'Are there differences in cognitive and spatial performance between retrolental and non-retrolental congenitally blind children?', paper submitted (15 December 1989) to *Journal of Visual Impairment & Blindness*.

MOBILITY AIDS FOR VISUALLY IMPAIRED PEOPLE

Researcher(s):   Dr B. Thomas
c/o Bristol Royal Society for the Blind
Stillhouse Lane
Bedminster, Bristol BS3 4EB
Tel: 0117 953 7750

Abstract:

Aims: To develop a mobility aid for use by people with sight problems, using video cameras and portable computers. Initial study to establish viability.

Methods: Use of technology appropriate to the development of the mobility aid.

Current status: Data collection and analysis under way.

Summary of findings:

Subjects of study: Visually impaired people who could use such a device not only to avoid obstructions in their paths but also to interpret them.

Coverage:

Timescale: 1 September 1989 - 30 September 1990.

Cost:

Funding body/bodies: Bristol Royal Society for the Blind (£1,000 bursary); Guide Dogs for the Blind Association (£4,000); other sources.

Report(s):

MOBILITY RELATED FEELINGS AND THE WALKING SPEED OF VISUALLY IMPAIRED TRAVELLERS

Researcher(s):   Dr W.D. Alan Beggs
Blind Mobility Research Unit
Department of Psychology
University of Nottingham
University Park, Nottingham NG7 2RD
Tel: 0115 951 5315

Abstract:

Evaluation indices for partially sighted travellers have been under development at BMRU. One of these, the percentage of preferred walking speed
(PPWS), was thought to be associated with some psychological factors such
as confidence and stress. Unfortunately, we had previously been unable
to show this to be the case. Using a more valid instrument than previously to measure confidence and stress, this study sought to choose between
this hypothesis and one which proposed that slower walking speed is a
function of reduced information pick-up due to visual impairment.

Methods: Partially sighted clients were asked to walk a short test route.
Their mobility related feelings were then assessed (see entry [3(c)2]) and
their PPWS was also measured. PPWS was then related to their feelings
and to their visual status.

Current status: Study completed; report in revision stage.

Summary of findings:

A multiple linear regression analysis of feelings and visual status on PPWS
showed that clinical measures of both visual acuity and field loss were
unrelated to PPWS, either directly or through their correlation with
feelings. Five of the mobility related feelings (feeling disorientated, being
on your guard, feeling confused, feeling that things were out of control,
and feeling incapable) together accounted for over sixty-three per cent of
the variance of this index. Although traditional measures of visual status
failed to enter the multiple regression until late, it was found that the
highest single correlation with visual status was lower peripheral field loss;

on its own, this accounted for twelve per cent of the variance of the PPWS measure, and had low correlations with the mobility related feelings. The information needed for locomotion largely comes from the lower peripheral field. The choice of a slower than normal walking speed therefore seems to be in part the way partially sighted - and possibly totally blind - pedestrians cope with the stress of travel, although a small proportion of the variance is accounted for by the loss of important visual input.

Subjects of study: Fifty-one partially sighted clients took part in walking a test route and completing a questionnaire on their feelings in relation to the experience.

Coverage:

Timescale: January 1988 - December 1988.
12 researcher weeks.

Cost: £6,140.

Funding body/bodies: Part of core programme.

Report(s):   Beggs, W.D.A., 'The correlates of walking speed in the visually impaired', paper accepted, following revisions, by *Ergonomics* (1990).

OBSTACLE LOCATION WITHOUT VISION

Researcher(s):   Dr Anthony J. Doyle, Ms Michelle D. Lee
and Carl Espin
Blind Mobility Research Unit
Department of Psychology
University of Nottingham
University Park, Nottingham NG7 2RD
Tel: 0115 951 5315

Abstract:

Some mobility officers feel that putting their partially sighted clients under a 'sleeper' blindfold helps the acquisition of auditory location skills. However, some partially sighted clients are reluctant to wear such a blindfold. The question therefore arose as to the influence that a blindfold actually has on the acquisition of auditory location skills. If it makes no difference there is nothing to be gained from trying to persuade reluctant clients to use a blindfold; if, on the other hand, there is an advantage, then perhaps a case should be made for putting all partially sighted clients under a blindfold for part of their mobility training.

Methods: The original intention was to train three groups of subjects to a standard on an audio location task: one under blindfold, the second without blindfolds, and a control group. Performances on the final test would indicate whether training under blindfold gave an advantage or not.

Current status: First phase completed and written up.

Summary of findings:

Phase 1: The first group of ten subjects all reached the criterion so quickly that it was clear the logic of the experiment was confounded; for if naïve subjects reached criterion with little or no practice it would not be possible to compare the effect of the blindfold as originally intended. This unexpectedly good performance appeared to be due to a modification of the traditional obstacle detection task.

Phase 2: Observations made during the obstacle location task led to further experiments which have shown that small oscillations in the time delay between two identical sound sources produces a very powerful response from subjects who describe the experience as being very similar to that associated with locating the obstacle at the side of the walkway. This will be explored further with the subjects used in the first experiment.

Subjects of study:	University undergraduate students.

Coverage:

Timescale:	Commenced 24 October 1989. Phase 1 end date 20 December 1989. Phase 2 end date July 1990 (est.).

Cost:	£15,600.

Funding body/bodies:	Part of core programme.

Report(s):	Although this experiment has not been completed in its original form, it is being written up for publication. The new technique reveals a standard of performance in this sort of task amongst the normal population which far exceeds that which had previously been thought possible.

PRELIMINARY COMPARISON OF EXPERT AND POOR TRAVELLERS' ABILITIES TO COPE WITH INDEPENDENT TRAVEL

Researcher(s): Dr W.D. Alan Beggs
Blind Mobility Research Unit
Department of Psychology
University of Nottingham
University Park, Nottingham NG7 2RD
Tel: 0115 951 5315

Abstract:

Earlier qualitative work, and subsequent descriptive work (see entry [3(o)5]) convinced us that at least one of the reasons for successful travel is the possession of certain meta-cognitive skills. In this study, we sought to confirm this, by comparing very 'expert' independent travellers with a matched group of poor, dependent travellers. Each was given a number of tests designed to cover a wide range of possible personality differences and differences in meta-cognitive functioning. Each was asked to undertake identical journeys.

Two groups of eleven visually impaired people were matched for age, sex, visual status, age of onset; most were also matched for aetiology. They differed in travel frequency; at least two daily independent journeys versus no independent journeys in a typical week, even though all subjects had been trained in mobility skills. Each group has been given four questionnaires: Tennessee Self-Concept Scale (Fitts, 1965); the Locus of Control Scale (Rotter, 1966); selected personality factors adapted from the Sports Personality Questionnaire (Hardy and Bradley, 1986); and Emotional Management Skills and Self-Awareness Scale (Rushall, 1979).

Current status: Data collection complete; analysis complete; report at an advanced stage.

Summary of findings:

Self-concept variables, as measured by the Tennessee Self-Concept Scale, were not significantly different from the sighted norms for either group, who did not differ from each other. As would be expected, both groups were significantly greater externalizers than sighted people; however, they did not differ from each other. The other tests have no sighted norms with which to make comparison. Five personality factors - intrinsic and extrinsic motivation, perseverance, emotional control and resistance to stress - also failed to differentiate between the groups. However, there were highly significant differences between the groups on susceptibility to, and ability to manage stress. Ability to manage attention and confidence were not significantly different. Thus, at least one meta-cognitive skill appears to be related to travel frequency.

Subjects of study: Matched small samples, one of eleven expert and independent visually impaired travellers and one of eleven poor and dependent visually impaired travellers. The subjects were all on the Blind Register; they had all been given cane training suitable for their impairment.

Coverage:

Timescale: January 1988 - June 1989.
36 researcher weeks.

Cost: £18,320.

Funding body/bodies: Part of core programme.

Report(s):   Report in preparation.

TASK ANALYSIS OF MOBILITY

Researcher(s):   Dr W.D. Alan Beggs
Blind Mobility Research Unit
Department of Psychology
University of Nottingham
University Park, Nottingham NG7 2RD
Tel: 0115 951 5315

Abstract:

Before any informed judgement about useful selection and training procedures or equipment design can be made, a comprehensive analysis of the demands and skills of visually impaired mobility is necessary. Although mobility training seems originally to have been based on an intuitive breakdown of the perceptuo-motor skills needed for visually impaired travel, to our knowledge, no-one has attempted a rigorous cognitive task analysis. We have, however, made a number of preliminary investigations in the past.

Methods: Three sources of expert knowledge were used. These were experienced mobility officers, the tutors at two of the three centres where they are trained, and what we have called 'expert travellers'. The latter were totally blind and partially sighted people who independently travel to work in London or another large conurbation daily, and who undertake more extensive journeys at will. They thus represent a very small group of successful visually impaired travellers.

Current status: Report being written.

Summary of findings:

A cognitive task analysis is a way of describing the abilities and skills needed to perform a complex, relatively unstructured task such as mobility. Three hierarchical levels have been identified: core skills, basic travel techniques, and advanced travel techniques. Core skills are the underlying motor, perceptual, cognitive, social and meta-cognitive skills needed for effective travel; travel techniques draw upon these core skills as appropriate. At present, mobility training focuses almost exclusively on the first three of these. Basic travel techniques are the mobility and orientation competencies needed by a traveller to make simple journeys, either indoors or outdoors without crossing roads. This limited level of mobility is all that many social services department clients may need to attain. Advanced travel techniques include various methods of road crossing, and the use of public transport. Few clients will use these. The analysis is a comprehensive overview of what is needed to travel and for teaching more effective social skills, which are needed when dealing with the public.

Subjects of study: Sample of experienced mobility officers and tutors from two of the three training centres. Sample of 'expert' visually impaired travellers. The latter were either long cane travellers who were totally blind, or partially sighted people with combinations of acuity and field losses which placed them on the Register. This latter group used various types of cane, often depending on lighting conditions.

Coverage:

Timescale: 1 September 1989 - 30 April 1990. 30 researcher weeks.

Cost: £15,384.

Funding body/bodies: Part of core programme.

Report(s): In preparation.

USE OF MAPS AND GRAPHICS IN THE MOBILITY TRAINING OF YOUNG VISUALLY HANDICAPPED CHILDREN

Researcher(s):   Dr Christopher Spencer and Dr Mark Blades
Department of Psychology
University of Sheffield
PO Box 603, Psychology Building
Western Bank, Sheffield S10 2UR
Tel: 0114 276 8555 x 6556

Abstract:

Evaluation of the use of a range of mapping and other graphical techniques in establishing spatial competencies in young children, and their more specific use in the learning of mobility techniques.

Methods: Experimental and case study, for example: working with matched groups receiving different types of statistical displays; following progress of individual children; and evaluating existing and new educational techniques against criteria.

Current status: Negotiation.

Summary of findings:

Subjects of study: Primary school children, aged 5-12 years.

Coverage:

Timescale: 1 October 1990 - 31 December 1993.
1 full-time postgraduate student throughout.

Cost:

Funding body/bodies: ESRC - grant awarded May 1990, but detailed funding not finalized.

Report(s):   Earlier work by the group summarized in Spencer, C.P., Blades, M. and Morsley, K. (1989), *Children in the Physical Environment*, Wiley, Chichester, Chapter 10.

VISUAL BALANCE CONTROL

Researcher(s):   Dr Anthony J. Doyle, Ms Michelle D. Lee
and Carl Espin
Blind Mobility Research Unit
Department of Psychology
University of Nottingham
University Park, Nottingham NG7 2RD
Tel: 0115 951 5315

Abstract:

This work is related to the work being done on the new 'Ocula' program. Some partially sighted people with a fairly good performance in static tasks in the foveal region report difficulties with mobility tasks. It is not generally known to what extent peripheral visual input controls balance, but Lee showed that a gentle oscillation of his swinging room induced a similar response in subjects although they were quite unconscious of any movement. This gives a precise measure of subject response to various stimuli.

Methods: A miniaturized version of Lee's swinging room has been built here at BMRU, to which an 'empty field' stimulus is being fitted. This consists of a featureless sphere on the inner surface of which various textures can be presented at different densities in different parts of the visual field. Both 'room' and subject movement are recorded in a form suitable for analysis in the Unit's statistical package.

Current status: The apparatus is already working and the sphere should be ready for the first recordings after the Easter break, 1990.

Summary of findings:

Subjects of study: Normative data will come from undergraduates and sixth form school children. Some partially sighted people may also be tested.

Coverage:

Timescale: March 1990 - July 1990 (est.).

Cost: £15,600.

Funding body/bodies: Part of core programme.

Report(s):

EVALUATION OF ASSESSMENT PROCEDURES AT THE RNIB REHABILITATION CENTRE, TORQUAY

Researcher(s): Dr Allan G. Dodds and Alistair P.D. Gaskell
Blind Mobility Research Unit
Department of Psychology
University of Nottingham
University Park, Nottingham NG7 2RD
Tel: 0115 951 5315

Ms Deborah J. Hellawell
(subsequently University of Durham
Tel: 0191 374 2000)

Abstract:

Aims: To evaluate the current assessment procedures at the Royal National Institute for the Blind's Employment Rehabilitation Centre at Manor House, Torquay.

Methods: Interviews with staff and clients; observations of assessment procedures.

Current status: Completed.

Summary of findings:

The aims of assessment were unclear and staff did not appear to understand their roles in the process. Information was not co-ordinated and no single individual appeared to be responsible for setting clients' programmes. Recommendations were made to improve the situation.

Subjects of study:	Blind and partially sighted people.

Coverage:

Timescale:	1 May 1988 - 15 May 1988.
	6 researcher weeks.

Cost:	£2,300.

Funding body/bodies:

Report(s):	BMRU Report No. 209, July 1988 (not for external circulation).

IDENTIFICATION OF POTENTIAL CONFUSIONS
IN LESSON ANALYSIS SCHEDULE

Researcher(s):   Dr W.D. Alan Beggs and Alistair P.D. Gaskell
Blind Mobility Research Unit
Department of Psychology
University of Nottingham
University Park, Nottingham NG7 2RD
Tel: 0115 951 5315

Abstract:

An experiment to develop more reliable methods of lesson analysis in relation to the work of mobility officers. One weakness in our earlier work on lesson analysis was the fact that a single encoder had been used; an inter-rater reliability check is an important method of validating a coding schedule. Inter-rater reliability had earlier been estimated at between eighty-five and ninety-two per cent, by a somewhat unsatisfactory method; one coder had re-scored the other's work, and thus had sight of his or her initial categorizations. A second weakness was that many of the coding criteria were only implicitly known to the two encoders now involved. It was important to make sure that these criteria matched and thus could be made explicit, so that others could also use the system. The experiment was designed to address both of these problems.

Methods: In order to compute inter-rater reliability coefficients, two encoders independently scored samples of three previously unseen lessons, with apparently very different styles. A matrix of categories was constructed, and each rater's codings entered into it. In this way, it would be possible not only to compute overall inter-rater reliabilities, but also to identify those categorizations where variation was lowest.

Current status: Completed.

Summary of findings:

Overall inter-rater reliability measured as indicated was lower than hoped, varying between 69.4 and 87.0 per cent. However, by using the matrix, common mismatches were identified; they were almost entirely due to confusions in one or two of the criteria for scoring, which thus needed to be made more explicit before a coding manual could be written. At this point, the part-time expert scorer left the BMRU, and rather than retrain another part-timer, a decision was made to wait until a new full-time member of staff was appointed. This was delayed for several months, until April 1987, but overall inter-rater reliability was subsequently confirmed at 73.3 per cent using an identical procedure.

Subjects of study: Two expert encoders independently coded four samples of lessons from three mobility officers.

Coverage:

Timescale: January 1986 - December 1989.
90 researcher weeks.

Cost: £46,000.

Funding body/bodies: Part of core programme.

Report(s): Gaskell, A.P.D. (1988), *The training styles project: a discussion paper*, BMRU Report No. 208 (for internal circulation only).

INVESTIGATION OF MOBILITY OFFICERS' ASSESSMENTS OF CLIENTS' NEEDS FOR TRAINING

Researcher(s): Dr W.D. Alan Beggs
Blind Mobility Research Unit
Department of Psychology
University of Nottingham
University Park, Nottingham NG7 2RD
Tel: 0115 951 5315

Abstract:

Previous work by BMRU found that assessments of training needs by mobility officers were unreliable, and probably invalid. We were unable to say how they actually did their assessments. This study was an attempt to confirm that their judgements were largely intuitive, rather than based on rational analysis of a client's strengths and weaknesses. We focused on partially sighted clients, mainly because training centre input in this area has been lacking in the past.

Methods: A correlation technique was used. We were able to relate training priority judgements made at RNIB, Manor House, Torquay, to existing data on clients' feelings about themselves and their mobility (see entries [3(c)2] and [3(o)2]), and to visual status.

Current status: Completed.

Summary of findings:

Training priority ratings given by the staff at RNIB, Manor House, were related to six of the mobility related feelings (feeling vulnerable, disorientated, not self-confident, conspicuous, and being wary and alert) and one measure of visual function. The emotional correlates are drawn from all three of the orthogonal factors in the mobility related feelings model. Acuity measures were unrelated to training priorities, as were overall measures of field loss. These latter two were available to staff from BD8 records, but were not used, even though they claimed that this was the case. However, lower peripheral field loss correlated quite highly with priorities, but could not have been directly known to staff. We believe that

209

this correlation occurred because of some intervening variable, such as clumsiness; information from the lower peripheral field is particularly important for locomotion. Assessments thus appear to be largely based on staff picking up how clients feel, and judging their initial travel ability; the seven items accounted for over seventy-five per cent of the variance of priorities.

Subjects of study: Fifty-one partially sighted clients at RNIB, Manor House, Torquay.

Coverage:

Timescale: January 1988 - December 1988.
12 researcher weeks.

Cost: £6,140.

Funding body/bodies: Part of core programme.

Report(s):   Beggs, W.D.A., 'How Mobility Officers assess the need for mobility training', paper submitted (20 December 1989) to *Journal of Vision Rehabilitation*.

LOW VISION ASSESSMENT AND TRAINING

Researcher(s):   Dr Allan G. Dodds
                   Blind Mobility Research Unit
                   Department of Psychology
                   University of Nottingham
                   University Park, Nottingham NG7 2RD
                   Tel: 0115 951 5315

                   Denis P. Davis (p-t postgraduate student)
                   RNIB Employment Rehabilitation Centre
                   Manor House, Middle Lincombe Road
                   Torquay, Devon TQ1 2NG
                   Tel: 01803 214523

Abstract:

Aims: To develop a battery of computer based visual assessment and training tasks, in order to improve the visual control of locomotion.

Methods: Experimental, involving four experimental and two control groups, each of ten subjects.

Current status: Completed.

Summary of findings:

Computer based visual tasks are better predictors of mobility performance than acuity data. Repeated practice at the tasks improves performance, and this transfers to real life mobility.

Subjects of study:	Registered blind and partially sighted people.
Coverage:	
Timescale:	1 January 1985 - 31 December 1987. 104 researcher weeks.
Cost:	£37,440.
Funding body/bodies:	Part of core programme.
Report(s):	Dodds, A.G. and Davis, D.P. (1988), 'Low vision: functional assessment and training', in Neustadt-Noy, N., Merin, S. and Schiff, Y. (eds), *Orientation and Mobility of the Visually Impaired* (Proc. of Fourth International Mobility Conference, held May 1986, Jerusalem), Heiliger, Jerusalem, pp. 29-34.
	Dodds, A.G. and Davis, D.P. (1989), 'Assessment and training of low vision clients for mobility', *Journal of Visual Impairment & Blindness*, vol. 83, no. 9, pp. 439-46.

THE MANUAL DEXTERITY OF VISUALLY HANDICAPPED ADULTS - NORMATIVE DATA

Researcher(s): Michael J. Tobin and Robert Greenhalgh
Research Centre for the Education of the Visually
Handicapped, School of Education,
University of Birmingham, Edgbaston
Birmingham B15 2TT
Tel: 0121 414 6737

Abstract:

Aims: The development and validation of methods of assessing manipulative skills among visually impaired adults, so that vocational rehabilitation officers can make reliable and objective judgements of existing levels of proficiency.

Methods: 991 subjects were tested on the various sub-scales of the Purdue Pegboard, the subjects being categorized on the basis of gender and degree of residual vision (six sub-groups).

Current status: Completed.

Summary of findings:

Gender (females superior) and degree of residual vision were found to be the significant independent variables. The ensuing statistical tables allow comparisons to be made with sighted and visually impaired people of the same, and differing, visual status. Suggestions/recommendations are made as to how the normative data may be used and as to the other kinds of information that can be derived by an observant and experienced tester.

Subjects of study:	Age range: 17-62 years. All subjects attending a specialist employment rehabilitation centre for visually impaired people of working age.
Coverage:	
Timescale:	1 January 1979 - 30 June 1987. 108 researcher weeks.
Cost:	
Funding body/bodies:	University of Birmingham (Senior Researcher's time); RNIB (second Researcher's time).
Report(s):	Tobin, M.J. and Greenhalgh, R. (1987), 'Normative data for assessing the manual dexterity of visually handicapped adults in vocational rehabilitation', *Journal of Occupational Psychology*, vol. 60, pp. 73-80.

ROLE-PLAY OF DIFFERENT TRAINING STYLES

Researcher(s):   Dr W.D. Alan Beggs
                   Blind Mobility Research Unit
                   Department of Psychology
                   University of Nottingham
                   University Park, Nottingham NG7 2RD
                   Tel: 0115 951 5315

Abstract:

In early work, we found that most mobility officers we sampled used a training style which was heavily biased towards 'telling'; this we have described as a 'trainer centred' or 'autocratic' style. Our belief was that this would have an effect both on the emergence of meta-cognitive strategies which might enable travellers to develop independence of their trainer, and at a motivational level, so that their perceived self-efficacy to solve travel problems was not maximized. We therefore needed to confirm that a more 'client centred', or 'democratic' style would have a number of psychological benefits for the traveller, which would show up either directly or indirectly in measures of travel frequency and novelty.

Methods: We used a style of training technique developed by the Industrial Training Research Unit at Cambridge. This uses tapes and booklets as examples of 'telling' and 'asking' styles, and tape recorders as feedback devices to enable mobility officers to monitor and adapt their own style. Unfortunately, we found it very difficult to motivate working mobility officers to change their training style and to allow us to find out the consequences of this with real clients; accordingly, we asked staff at South Regional Association for the Blind to role-play two extreme styles with their students. We asked for qualitative comments, and used a prototype mobility related feelings questionnaire to try to pick up any psychological changes.

Current status: Completed.

Summary of findings:

Qualitative data from the students confirmed the small amount we had already gathered from visually impaired clients in the earlier study. The 'telling' style felt patronizing and not produce an improvement in self-confidence. It was a passive experience, leading to loss of concentration, and overloaded and interrupted learning, but was useful for facts and very basic techniques. The 'asking' style was felt to be a 'better', 'positive' experience, was more active and enjoyable to participate in, and improved self-confidence because success was self-generated. Data from the questionnaire failed to show any difference between the two styles.

Subjects of study: Sample of staff and students at SRAB, using role-play and a questionnaire, plus data from visually impaired clients from an earlier study. Sighted trainee mobility officers, operating under simulated sight loss spectacles and blindfolds.

Coverage:

Timescale: 1 March 1987 - 31 March 1987.
2 researcher weeks.

Cost: £1,025.

Funding body/bodies: Part of core programme.

Report(s):   *Report to the Chief Scientist, Research Management Division, Department of Health & Social Security, covering the period 1 April 1984 to 31 March 1988, including future proposals,* July 1988, pp. 50-8.

'BEYOND VISION: TRAINING FOR WORKERS IN VISUAL IMPAIRMENT'

Researcher(s):   Karen Maychell and David Smart
National Foundation for Educational Research
The Mere, Upton Park
Slough, Berkshire SL1 2DQ
Tel: 01753 574123

Abstract:

A comprehensive study of the training provided for mobility officers and technical officers and the work carried out by them.

Aims: To clarify how the training relates to the requirements of the work, within the twin contexts of social services department provision and the needs of visually impaired people. This included an examination of the training courses, student characteristics and recruitment, and the work and working environment of practising mobility officers and technical officers.

Methods: Detailed study of the training courses themselves, which involved reviewing documentation and exploring the format and scope of planned initiatives. Also, training course staff, students, and workers who had recently completed a training course were interviewed. Investigation of student characteristics and recruitment. This involved a questionnaire to all mobility officers and technical officers and interviews with training agency staff and students. Study of the work and working environment. On the basis of information obtained from the questionnaire, a sample of mobility officers and technical officers was interviewed. This was chosen to reflect variations in working environments, amount of specialist work done, and (recent) date of training. From the interviews a sub-sample of six locations was selected for intensive case studies. This allowed a closer examination of the different kinds of working environment which exist and their implications for mobility officers and technical officers. The case studies involved further interviews with the specialists themselves, observation of them at work, and interviews with colleagues, managers and clients.

Current status: Completed.

Summary of findings:

The majority of specialist workers are mobility officers and technical officers; three-quarters are employed by social services departments and the rest by voluntary organizations and local education authorities (all this at the time of the study). There are no common standards of client/ worker ratios, or integration and supervision within agencies. Demand for services is more limited than training presumes - the majority of clients are elderly and their motivation is affected by a variety of factors.

Conclusions: Training emphasized students learning the skills clients need rather than how to transmit the skills, and emphasized work with totally blind rather than partially sighted clients. Training was based on the assumption that clients are motivated to learn. Students had mixed attitudes to counselling but it is an important precursor to rehabilitation. There was little evidence of joint approaches and standards in the new rehabilitation officer training. There was a need to improve organization and deployment of staff in the work setting. The role of specialist workers was limited by low status in relation to other SSD and health colleagues.

Subjects of study:	Mobility officers and technical officers trained to work with visually impaired people by the NRAB, the SRAB and the NMC, plus staff and current students at the three training centres.
Coverage:	
Timescale:	1988-89.
Cost:	£100,000 approx.
Funding body/bodies:	Department of Health.
Report(s):	Maychell, K. and Smart, D. (1990), *Visual impairment training reviewed*, NFER.
	Maychell, K. and Smart, D. (1990), *Beyond Vision: Training for workers in visual impairment*, NFER/Nelson, London.

ACCESS TO INFORMATION AND LEARNING BY VISUALLY HANDICAPPED PEOPLE THROUGH MICRO-COMPUTER TECHNOLOGY

Researcher(s): Michael J. Tobin, Paul Blenkhorn, Malcolm Ross,
Simon Spencer, A. Hawley and S. Jefferys
Research Centre for the Education of the Visually
Handicapped, School of Education
University of Birmingham, Edgbaston
Birmingham B15 2TT
Tel: 0121 414 6737

Abstract:

Aims: To produce micro-computer software that will allow blind and partially sighted people of all ages to have access to the same information as their fully sighted peers. Using commercially available hardware (including such peripherals as touch sensitive screens, concept keyboards, joy-sticks, visual display units), the programme - a long-term one - hopes to demonstrate the potential of information technology as a means of overcoming many of the disabling consequences (educational and vocational) of visual impairment.

Methods: Exploring, with visually impaired clients and their advisers, their immediate needs in education and employment (involving meetings and a 'Newsletter'). Drawing up specifications for specific software programs. Field trials of the materials (in pre-school playgroups, schools and work-places).

Current status: Ongoing development of software. Papers being published on various aspects of project (see below).

Summary of findings:

There are now over forty programs in trials or in regular daily use by children and adults in work. The value of the materials may be gauged by the fact that some 120 or so programs are being sent out (at cost) each month to users in schools and workplaces.

Subjects of study:	Age range: 18-months upwards. All subjects registered as blind or partially sighted, including those with additional impairments.

Coverage:

Timescale:	Commenced 1 September 1982; continuing.

Cost:	Approx. £35,000 per annum (excluding Director's time - paid by University of Birmingham).

Funding body/bodies:	Mainly RNIB, with assistance for equipment from other charities and the University.

Report(s):	Blenkhorn, P. and Tobin, M. (1984), 'Using computers with the less able deaf-blind', *SENSE Newsletter*, vol. 30, no. 2, p. 6.
	Blenkhorn, P. and Payne, B. (1985), 'Teletext for the visually impaired', *New Beacon*, vol. 69, no. 819, pp. 197-8.
	Hawley, A., Jefferys, S., Ross, M., Spencer, S. and Tobin, M.J. (1987), 'Electronic publishing and visually handicapped learners', *New Beacon*, vol. 71, no. 844, pp. 253-5.
	Spencer, S. and Ross, M. (1988), 'Visual stimulation using micro-computers', *European Journal of Special Education*, vol. 3, no. 3, pp. 173-6.
	Spencer, S. and Ross, M. (1989), 'Closing the gap', *Special Children*, no. 28, pp. 20-21.
	Spencer, S. and Ross, M. (1989), 'Software packages for the young visually handicapped', *Special Children*, no. 31, pp. 20-21.
	Spencer, S. and Ross, M. (1989), 'Assessing functional vision using microcomputers', *British Journal of Special Education*, vol. 16, no. 2, pp. 68-70.

EVALUATION OF A LOW VISION TRAINING PROGRAMME

Researcher(s): John Collins
Partially Sighted Society
Sight Centre, Dean Clarke House
Southernhay East
Exeter, Devon EX1 1PE
Tel: 01392 210656

Abstract:

The major cause of visual impairment in the UK is age related macular degeneration. This leads to major problems in terms of performing near vision tasks such as reading, sewing etc. A method of helping MD sufferers to improve their near vision performance is to teach 'eccentric fixation', by which the individual is assisted to use a para-jovial area of the retina to replace the disordered macula.

Methods: Joint research project using visually impaired people who attend PSS Low Vision Services.

Current status: Pilot study currently in progress.

Summary of findings:

Subjects of study:	Elderly people suffering age related macular degeneration, who attend PSS Low Vision Services.
Coverage:	
Timescale:	1 February 1990 - 31 May 1992.
Cost:	Salaries in excess of £30,000; travel £5,000.
Funding body/bodies:	Externally funded.
Report(s):	Paper to be offered to the International Conference on Low Vision Rehabilitation in Holland, 1993.

PSYCHOLOGICAL ADJUSTMENT TO SIGHT LOSS

Researcher(s): Dr A.G. Dodds, Ms Janet H. Cooper
and Ms Michelle D. Lee
Blind Mobility Research Unit
Department of Psychology
University of Nottingham
University Park, Nottingham NG7 2RD
Tel: 0115 951 5315

Abstract:

Development of reliable and valid versions of existing personality and attitude questionnaires, including: self-esteem; self-efficacy; locus of control; acceptance of visual handicap; anxiety and depression; attributional style.

Aims: To predict final rehabilitation outcome and to identify clients with specific motivational and attitudinal problems.

Methods: Cluster analysis; multiple linear regression; factor analysis; item analysis; coefficient alpha.

Current status: Data collection and analysis in progress. Paper being prepared.

Summary of findings:

Preliminary analysis suggests that the factors under investigation form a tight cluster, with all factors directly or indirectly associated with each other. Factor analysis shows that all questionnaire scores load on to one factor, accounting for fifty-eight per cent of the variance. This factor has been labelled 'psychological well-being'.

Subjects of study:	Age: 18-90 years. Blind and partially sighted.
Coverage:	
Timescale:	1 September 1989 - 31 December 1991 (est.). 150 researcher weeks.
Cost:	£37,500.
Funding body/bodies:	Part of core programme.
Report(s):	Dodds, A.G. (1989), 'Motivation reconsidered: the importance of self-efficacy variables in rehabilitation', *British Journal of Visual Impairment*, vol. 7, no. 1, pp. 7-10. Further manuscript in preparation for publication.

USING SIGHTED VOLUNTEERS FOR TEACHING MOON TO NEWLY BLINDED ADULTS

Researcher(s): Michael J. Tobin and Eileen W. Hill
Research Centre for the Education of the Visually
Handicapped, School of Education
University of Birmingham, Edgbaston
Birmingham B15 2TT
Tel: 0121 414 6737

Abstract:

Aims: To assess the feasibility of using sighted volunteers to teach Moon, an alternative tactile medium to Braille, to newly blinded adults.

Methods: One-day training courses, in which ten pairs of sighted and blind volunteers are taught to read and write Moon, using face-to-face teaching and specially written print and tactile materials. Questionnaire evaluation at end of each training course.

Current status: Courses and evaluation continuing.

Summary of findings:

The considerable amount of learning achieved by blind and sighted volunteers leads us to judge that this is an efficient and cost-effective procedure for developing written communication skills among newly blinded adults, enabling professional rehabilitation workers to use their time and skills more economically and giving the community at large the opportunity to participate in the whole rehabilitation process.

Subjects of study:	Blind adults (previously print readers) of any age; sighted volunteers. No previous experience of Moon needed.

Coverage:

Timescale:	Commenced 1 January 1986; continuing. Three weeks per annum (excluding time for writing and field-testing the teaching materials - approx. six months).

Cost:

Funding body/bodies:	University of Birmingham (Senior Researcher's time); RNIB (second Researcher's time).

Report(s):	Tobin M.J. and Hill E.W. (1989), 'Harnessing the community: Moon script, the Moon-writer, and sighted volunteers', *British Journal of Visual Impairment*, vol. 7, no. 1, pp. 3-5.

WELFARE OF THE VISUALLY IMPAIRED:
DAILY LIVING SKILLS AND INDEPENDENCE

Researcher(s):   Via General Secretary
Surrey Voluntary Association for the Blind
'Rentwood', School Lane, Fetcham
Leatherhead, Surrey KT22 9JX
Tel: 01372 377701

Abstract:

Study of visually impaired persons in the County of Surrey.

Aims: To improve daily living skills and to lead to a greater degree of independence.

Methods: One-to-one instruction in a Resource Centre, Low Vision Aids Centre.

Current status: Ongoing: a day-to-day development.

Summary of findings:

Subjects of study:	Registered blind and partially sighted people.
Coverage:	Within County boundary of Surrey, at the centres specified, all registered partially sighted and technically blind clients receiving instruction in daily living skills.
Timescale:	
Cost:	
Funding body/bodies:	
Report(s):	Annual reports, internal financial reports, and reports to Surrey Social Services Department. Also available to any other organizations concerned with the interests of visually impaired people.

'BREAKING THROUGH: DEVELOPING SERVICES FOR DEAF-BLIND PEOPLE'

Researcher(s):   Deaf-Blind Services Liaison Group (RNIB, NDBL, SENSE, RNID), representatives of ADSS, AMA and ACC
c/o Royal National Institute for the Blind
224 Great Portland Street
London W1N 6AA
Tel: 0171 388 1266

Abstract:

Aims: To comment as appropriate on services currently available to deaf-blind people, as germane to the framing of recommendations for the future. To identify the principles on which services for deaf-blind people and their supporters should be based. To make recommendations on the application of those principles by local authorities.

Methods: The DBSLG initiated a working group, which included representatives of the two main local authority associations, the Association of Directors of Social Services, and deaf-blind people. The group reviewed the legislation concerning its target group, identified needs, and made recommendations for meeting these.

Current status: Report, *Breaking Through*, published September 1988.

Summary of findings:

Draws together available data on potential size and nature of deaf-blind population. Previous lack of such information has led to failure to develop appropriate services. Need to develop a philosophy and strategy of service for this group, to raise standards of assessment, to adopt a multi-disciplinary approach, and to ensure adequate staff training.

Regarding specific areas of service: social workers should ensure that deaf people have their sight and blind people their hearing regularly tested, and that any secondary sensory impairment should lead to referral for appropriate help; each SSD should establish a Standing Forum to develop a comprehensive strategy and action plan.

| **Subjects of study:** | For the purposes of the report, persons are regarded as deaf-blind if they have a severe degree of combined visual and auditory impairment resulting in problems of communication, information and mobility. This includes people with severe vision and hearing impairment since birth or early childhood, people who develop dual impairment in later life, and people who function as vision and hearing impaired. |

Coverage:

| **Timescale:** | October 1987 - September 1988.
10 researcher weeks plus travelling time. |

| **Cost:** | £8,000. |

| **Funding body/bodies:** | Deaf-Blind Services Liaison Group. |

| **Report(s):** | *Breaking Through: Developing Services for Deaf-Blind People* is available from: |

RNID   0171 387 8033
RNIB   0171 388 1266
SENSE   0171 272 7724

Single copies are free; additional copies £2.50p. each.

FEASIBILITY STUDY FOR A COUNTY-WIDE SERVICE FOR DEAF-BLIND PEOPLE

Researcher(s):   George Chapman
Social Services Department
Norfolk County Council
County Hall, Martineau Lane
Norwich NR1 2DH
Tel: 01603 223145

Abstract:

Based on SSI reports.

Aims: To identify deaf-blind people as clients. To assess their needs. To recruit, train and deploy guide-helps to meet these needs. Particular attention paid to rural areas, as they are less well served than the urban area of Norwich.

Methods: Consultation with SSD staff, SRAB, NDBL, Education Officers, existing and potential consumers. Comparison with services in other local authorities. Observation of deaf-blind care in residential homes and long-stay hospitals.

Current status: Completed.

Summary of findings:

SSD staff response ambivalent - recognized need for service but feared increase in workload in some area teams because of lack of resources or expertise. Client Record System generally not adequate to identify this client group - no specific category.

Local voluntary organizations felt services needed improving - registration as blind or partially sighted seen as giving deaf-blind clients access to a greater range of resources than registration as deaf.

Mobility officers acknowledged their training was not appropriate for deaf-blind clients because they relied on clients' hearing abilities.

Residential/nursing home staff find this client group has very high level of needs and feel unable to meet them, due to lack of time and training.

Recommendations: SSD budget to recruit and train guide-helpers, delegating responsibility to Norwich Institution for the Blind. Also revision of client categories on SSD register.

Subjects of study: Deaf-blind people identified through the SSD Client Record System. Workers as listed under Methods.

Coverage: Clients, professional staff, several local and national voluntary organizations. Report includes brief information on the provision of services to deaf-blind people provided by other local authorities.

Timescale: 4 April 1986 - 28 April 1986.

Cost:

Funding body/bodies:

Report(s):   Report available from Norfolk Social Services Department.

REVIEW OF SERVICES FOR HEARING IMPAIRED AND VISUALLY HANDICAPPED PEOPLE

Researcher(s): Directorate of Housing and Personal Services,
Bexley London Borough
Bexley Civic Offices, Broadway
Bexleyheath, Kent DA6 7LB
Tel: 0181 303 7777

Abstract:

Report to the Housing and Personal Services Committee: review of services and proposals for future development.

Methods: Analysis of data available on clients with hearing and visual impairments. Information from Departmental records and from other relevant local agencies. Analysis of data on staff providing services for these client groups. Analysis of resources and roles of local voluntary organizations, including reference to the Kent Association for the Blind (see also entry [1B(o)4]). Analysis of local health services for these client groups.

Current status: Completed.

Summary of findings:

As statutory registers do not require registration of client numbers, they underestimate the potential size of the relevant population in the Borough with a sight or hearing loss. The majority of the people affected are elderly. Present services are of high quality but limited quantity.
   The report identified a number of avenues for service development; most having financial implications.

Recommendations: Included development of two separate specialist sections within Social Services Department; development of a resource centre; further development of collaboration with local voluntary organizations; joint developments with Bexley Health Authority.

Subjects of study:	Clients of the Department who were registered in December 1987 as blind, partially sighted, deaf without speech, deaf with speech, or hard of hearing.
Coverage:	Existing clients registered with the Social Services Department, London Borough of Bexley.
Timescale:	Late 1987 - April 1988 (report presented to Committee April 1988).
Cost:	
Funding body/bodies:	
Report(s):	Internal to SSD.

DEAF-BLIND SERVICES IN AVON

Researcher(s):   R.J.R. Hitchings
                   c/o Bristol Royal Society for the Blind
                   Stillhouse Lane
                   Bedminster, Bristol BS3 4EB
                   Tel: 0117 953 7750

Abstract:

Aims: To examine service provision for people with both visual and hearing impairments.

Methods: Collation of existing reports. Working Party on subject.

Current status: Analysis of data and report writing in progress.

Summary of findings:

Subjects of study: Registered blind and partially sighted people who also have severe hearing difficulties. All ages and conditions.

Coverage:

Timescale: 1 June 1989 - 30 January 1990 (est.).

Cost:

Funding body/bodies:

Report(s):   Will be available by end of January 1990.

EVALUATION OF SENSE MIDLANDS (FURTHER EDUCATION)
(Part of the National Deaf-Blind and Rubella Association)

Researcher(s):   Janet Cooper, Research Fellow
Eric Emerson, Senior Research Fellow (Co-ordinator)
Hester Adrian Research Centre
University of Manchester, Oxford Road
Manchester M13 9PL
Tel: 0161 275 3340

Abstract:

It would appear that SENSE Midlands (Further Education) may be more expensive to run than most of the long-stay institutions from which it draws its students. However, as the centre is unique it is not possible to undertake a detailed comparative analysis of its cost-effectiveness; instead the project will examine the quality of its provision and the outcome for its students.

Methods: Analysis of a group of eighteen potential students successfully referred but awaiting a vacancy. Analysis of a second group of people with special needs - severe behaviour problems, learning difficulties. Observation to assess engagement in activities. Monitoring social integration using diary format. Rate of skills and communication development over twelve months. Organizational aspects of quality of care.

Current status: Planning.

Summary of findings:

Subjects of study: SENSE students aged 19-50 years. Waiting list group may include slightly younger people.

Coverage: Students of SENSE Midlands (FE).

Timescale: Original schedule April 1990 - May 1992, but Research Fellow not in post until September 1990.

Cost: Estimated £56,000.

Funding body/bodies: Commissioned by the Department of Health.

Report(s):

IDENTIFYING NEEDS AND NUMBERS OF DEAF-BLIND IN DEVON

Researcher(s):   Peter Holman (Research Co-ordinator)
SENSE South West
Tel: 01626 64079

Geoff King (County Adviser)
Maxine Green (Information Officer)
Social Services Department
Devon County Council
County Hall, Topsham Road
Exeter EX2 4QR
Tel: 01392 382000

Abstract:

Aims: Identification of total numbers and needs of deaf-blind people in Devon, in order to plan for future service development and improvement.

Current status: Data collection/investigation under way.

Summary of findings:

Subjects of study:	Deaf-blind people.
Coverage:	County of Devon.
Timescale:	March 1990 - October 1990.
Cost:	£3000.
Funding body/bodies:	
Report(s):	Due October 1990. The information is to be presented to the Department in the form of:

Area Reports for each Social Services Area, with detail for each District in that Area, including the provision of a list of names of current or potential clients.

A County Report, giving the global picture of this client group and its needs, in order for the Department to plan for future services.

PROVISION OF SERVICES FOR DEAF-BLIND PEOPLE

Researcher(s):   Sunderland and Durham County Incorporated
Royal Institution for the Blind
8 Foyle Street, Sunderland
Tyne & Wear SR1 1LB
Tel: 0191 567 3939

(in collaboration with the local Social Services
Department)

Abstract:

In January 1988 the Borough of Sunderland held a Forum to consider the
recommendations of the report *Breaking Through* (see entry [5(c)1]). A
'Core Group' was set up.

Aims: To identify the number of people with a dual sensory impairment
living in the Borough of Sunderland; to examine ways of improving
services for deaf-blind people; to promote education and training in the
field of deaf-blindness; to review and monitor the implementation of
recommendations.

Current status:

Summary of findings:

Subjects of study: Deaf-blind people.

Coverage: Borough of Sunderland.

Timescale:

Cost:

Funding body/bodies:

Report(s):

REVIEW AND SURVEY OF THE PROVISION OF SERVICES TO PEOPLE WHO ARE DEAF-BLIND

Researcher(s): Contact: John Luke
Principal Officer
Community Disability Team
Social Services Division
Stockport Metropolitan Borough Council
Bamford Close, 31A Adswood Lane West
Calegreen, Stockport SK3 8HT
Tel: 0161 474 4678

Abstract:

In accordance with the recommendations of the report *Breaking Through* (see entry [5(c)1]), Stockport has established a Standing Forum to review Local Authority and Health Authority provision of services to people who have the substantial dual impairment of deafness and blindness.

Methods: Identification of numbers of people and degrees of impairment. Detailed questionnaire to be completed on the most severely impaired people identified. Collation, analysis and report of questionnaire findings. Conclusions and recommendations for service changes/improvements in Stockport to be presented to the two authorities.

Current status: Initial data collection almost complete. Questionnaire designed and ready for use.

Summary of findings:

Subjects of study:	Deaf-blind people of all ages, but especially interested in adults.
Coverage:	Area served by the MBC and DHA.
Timescale:	October 1989 - October 1990.
Cost:	
Funding body/bodies:	'In-house' study; costs shared by the members of the Forum, some of whom are professionals from various departments in MBC and DHA, some volunteers with a personal interest, some deaf-blind people themselves.
Report(s):	

DAY CARE FOR VISUALLY IMPAIRED PEOPLE WITH LEARNING DIFFICULTIES

Researcher(s):   Mrs Hanicra Haverlamp-Monks
c/o Bristol Royal Society for the Blind
Stillhouse Lane
Bedminster, Bristol BS3 4EB
Tel: 01495 220420 or via 0117 953 7750

Abstract:

Aims: To identify the number of people with the dual impairment, and their met and unmet needs regarding day care. To set up, run, and evaluate a day care project.

Methods: Questionnaires, personal interviews; later pilot project.

Current status: Report completed; seminars on report being run in Bristol; discussions on implications with Avon SSD.

Summary of findings:

A surprisingly small number of visually impaired people with learning difficulties live in the community in the area studied; however, there is no special service provision. A larger number are at present living in hospitals, but will be transferred to the community. Potential number leaving special schools is unknown.

Identification of need: questionnaires returned by the Community Mental Handicap Teams, Hospitals, and Resource and Activity Centres gave a clear picture of a lack of specific services to meet the needs of the client group who were known to them. Very low response rate from Social Services Area Teams. Very few special schools replied, making it 'futile to predict' the numbers of doubly impaired children requiring specialist day care in future.

Main needs identified: lack of training for staff, inadequate staffing levels, lack of information, lack of specialist staff, lack of awareness of visual impairment, lack of eye testing, lack of day care resources.

Day care project: run for fifteen weeks for six doubly impaired clients and one helper each. High staffing ratios necessary, along with extra training for these staff. Input from specialist staff necessary from time-to-time. Programme needs to be flexible to meet individual needs, but also must provide segregated and integrated group experiences. Venue and environment must take account of nature and range of impairments - should be specially adapted and provide appropriate equipment. All this requires adequate funding. Report concludes clients benefited from the experience, demonstrating continuing need for the service.

Subjects of study:	Visually impaired people with learning difficulties. Registered blind and partially sighted people - all conditions.
Coverage:	South Bristol.
Timescale:	1 October 1988 - 30 September 1989.
Cost:	
Funding body/bodies:	Bristol Royal Society for the Blind (£500 bursary); Avon Social Services Department.
Report(s):	Report published by the Bristol Royal Society for the Blind. Extracts may be published in the *British Journal of Visual Impairment*.

MENTALLY HANDICAPPED PEOPLE WITH HEARING AND SIGHT PROBLEMS

Researcher(s):   Stella O'Donnell
Senior Research and Information Officer,
Social Services Department
Cornwall County Council
County Hall, Station Road
Truro TR1 3AY
Tel: 01872 74282

Abstract:

Report based on information held on Cornwall's Mental Handicap Register, July 1989. Register records two levels of visual and aural problems: 'poor sight or hearing' and 'blind or almost blind and deaf or almost deaf'.

Current status: Completed.

Summary of findings:

Identified sixty-one people with learning difficulties and additional sight and hearing problems - five per cent of all people on the Mental Handicap Register. Three-quarters were recorded as with 'poor sight or hearing'; remainder either totally deaf and blind or deaf with poor sight, or blind with poor hearing.

Report identifies geographical distribution of client group throughout the County in terms of administrative areas, their types of accommodation, dependency categories, additional physical disabilities, behavioural problems, the pattern of elderly carers, provision of day care and of residential care.

Report concludes that communication problems are particularly severe for this client group, that they have a higher than average incidence of other problems, that most live at home with limited access to day care services, and that if more specialist help is to be made available it would most appropriately be situated in mid-Cornwall.

Subjects of study: Sixty-one people registered as having learning difficulties and with sight loss and hearing loss identified as additional impairments, representing just under five per cent of the people on Cornwall's Mental Handicap Register.

Coverage: County of Cornwall and as above.

Timescale:

Cost:

Funding body/bodies:

Report(s): Report, *Cornwall: Mental Handicap Register, 1989,* available from Cornwall Social Services Department.

'OUT OF ISOLATION: A PLAN FOR THE GROWTH OF SERVICES TO MULTI-HANDICAPPED VISUALLY IMPAIRED PEOPLE'

Researcher(s): Anthony Best, Paul Ennals, Peter Johnson
Royal National Institute for the Blind,
224 Great Portland Street,
London W1N 6AA
Tel: 0171 388 1266

Abstract:

Aims: To outline the needs of people in the 19-plus age group with multiple impairments including sight loss. To review present provision for them from all sources and identify gaps. To propose an overall strategy for meeting the needs of this group. To define a role for the RNIB within this strategy.

Methods: Commissioned a demographic review to establish numbers in this client group: Moss, J. (1985) *Third Demographic Study - visually handicapped people with additional disabilities: England,* RNIB. Also had an advisory group to support working party. Study in three phases: visits to and information from forty-plus relevant service providing settings; analysis of range of provision and examination of options for meeting needs; development of models for future services.

Current status: Completed.

Summary of findings:

Large gaps and inconsistencies in provision of services to this client group by health authorities, social services departments, voluntary organizations and other specialist agencies. Provision represents a very small part of SSD resources; NHS provision is mainly residential care for people with severe learning difficulties. Part of the problem is that the client group is not homogeneous in terms of patterns of multiple impairment, needs, age distribution or geographical distribution. Also lack of awareness of client group, and lack of means of identifying them, on the part of specialist services. Hence lack of co-ordination and development of appropriate services.

There are approximately 23,200 adults in Britain aged between sixteen and sixty-five years who in addition to sight problems have other impairments. Only 350 of them were in specialist settings.

Main areas of service need identified: residential accommodation, domiciliary support, day and evening provision (including rehabilitation), continuing education, advisory services (including assessment), and staff training and support.

Recommendations: Regional centres with residential and continuing education resources and multi-professional teams of advisers. These could be run by voluntary organizations and funded by health and social services. RNIB role, full or partial involvement in regional centres and provision of national training and information services. Regional centres and national service could be developed from base of existing resources.

Subjects of study:	Health, social services and voluntary organizations with clients with multiple impairments including sight loss. Congenitally multiply impaired people with visual impairments. Multiply impaired people with one or more acquired additional impairments. Age groups 16-20, 21-49 and 50-64 yrs.
Coverage:	National sample of statutory and non-statutory services.
Timescale:	
Cost:	
Funding body/bodies:	
Report(s):	Best, A.B., Ennals, P. and Johnson, P. (1987), *Out of Isolation: A Plan for the Growth of Services to Multi-Handicapped Visually Impaired People,* RNIB, London.

VISUAL ASSESSMENT AT THE WYVERN SPECIAL EDUCATION CENTRE, PEWSEY

Researcher(s):   Mrs Janet Duffield
c/o Bristol Royal Society for the Blind
Stillhouse Lane
Bedminster, Bristol BS3 4EB
Tel: 01672 62197 or via 0117 953 7750

Abstract:

Staff running a course for blind people at Wyvern Special Education Centre in Pewsey Hospital (Wilts) became aware of the high incidence of visual impairment amongst other hospital residents which had not been investigated. A major difficulty was how to test visually impaired people with severe learning difficulties.

Aims: To develop picture matching tests. To adapt a visual assessment checklist for visually impaired adults who function at a pre-verbal level. To gain more information about a newly developed photographic process for measuring the focal length of the eye, which might be appropriate for use with the client group.

Current status: Report completed. Further development work at Pewsey Hospital; discussions with Health Authorities in Bristol.

Summary of findings:

Picture matching tests: developed and extended system. Pre-verbal adults: tests developed to relate to everyday experiences which had meaning for the subjects - e.g. identification of favourite foods; level of understanding and involvement of key workers improved. Methods of assessment by specialists extended and four people referred to ophthalmic optician. Care staff now developing skills to identify where behaviour problems might be caused by sight difficulties or where they may have other causes.

Subjects of study:	Multiply-impaired residents at Pewsey Hospital, Wiltshire. Registered blind and partially sighted people of all ages and conditions.
Coverage:	
Timescale:	1 October 1988 - 30 September 1989.
Cost:	
Funding body/bodies:	Bristol Royal Society for the Blind (£500 bursary); Wyvern Special Education Centre, Pewsey Hospital.
Report(s):	Report published by Bristol Royal Society for the Blind. Extracts may be published in the *British Journal of Visual Impairment*.

SERVICES FOR MULTI-HANDICAPPED VISUALLY IMPAIRED PEOPLE

Researcher(s):   Mrs Diana Harries
South Regional Association for the Blind
55 Eton Avenue
London NW3 3ET
Tel: (Office) 0171 722 9703
    (Home) 0181 521 8729

[Note: SRAB 'dissolved' 1994.]

Abstract:

Aims: To assess, with the help of local services, the needs of people with multiple impairments who may require special provision because of their sight problems. To prepare, with the help of existing organizations, appropriate programmes, training and models of service, and to encourage their implementation. To identify skills and expertise, and to help research the resources necessary to develop services. To encourage the implementation of joint schemes (NHS, LA or voluntary sector). To recommend possible projects for the future, including the setting up of an advisory service.

Methods: Interviews, correspondence, extensive travelling.

Current status: Data collection in progress; analysis beginning.

Summary of findings:

Subjects of study:	Multiply-impaired people with sight loss. Base population people with learning difficulties and an additional sensory loss. In addition, those with a hearing loss and other physical disabilities are also included.
Coverage:	Nationally based study of subjects as outlined above.
Timescale:	7 December 1987 - 30 November 1990.
Cost:	£25,000 p.a. over 3 years (est.).
Funding body/bodies:	South East Thames Regional Health Authority, £15,000 p.a.; Department of Health, £10,000 p.a. A private charity has guaranteed any loss caused by expenditure over £25,000 p.a. (Funding administered by SRAB.)
Report(s):	

COMPARISON OF EDUCATION FACILITIES FOR VISUALLY IMPAIRED YOUNGSTERS IN CLYWD AND CHESHIRE

Researcher(s):   Mrs A.P. Walker
                  Chester Blind Welfare Society
                  67 Liverpool Road
                  Chester CH2 1AP
                  Tel: 01244 382222

Abstract:

Methods: Case studies of two visually impaired boys of similar age (six years). Research into structures and policies of local authorities through personal contact with managers and appropriate staff. Use of printed material from 'statementing' etc.

Current status: Completed.

Summary of findings:

The benefits of education in regular school are those of social integration with the child's peer group. The benefit of education in a specialist school is higher academic attainment as a result of the availability of appropriate equipment and the teaching of specialist skills, but with a risk of social isolation from the child's own wider community.

Subjects of study:	Education service in two local authorities via case studies of two six-year-old visually impaired boys.
Coverage:	Two case studies of individuals in different LAs.
Timescale:	February 1988 - August 1988.
Cost:	
Funding body/bodies:	'In-house' - part of Director's work.
Report(s):	Paper delivered to workshop, International Council for the Education of the Visually Handicapped Conference, 'Realities and Opportunities', 7-13 August 1988. Abstract available in Conference booklet.

FURTHER EDUCATION NEEDS, ACADEMIC AND SOCIAL, OF THE BLIND AND PARTIALLY SIGHTED

Researcher(s): Dr Gill MacDonagh,
Wild Orchard, South Harting
Petersfield, Hants GU31 5PY
Tel: 01730 825512

and c/o Royal London Society for the Blind
105 Salusbury Road
London NW6 6RH
Tel: 0171 624 8844

Abstract:

Aims: To assess the problems encountered in the community by school leavers. To facilitate changes in teaching methods in the school's Further Education Unit to meet the problems identified.

Methods: In-depth audio taped interviews with about thirty ex-pupils of Dorton House School for the Blind, Sevenoaks, in their own homes. Interviews focused around 'a typical day', using specially designed schedule as an *aide memoire*.

Current status: Planning.

Summary of findings:

Subjects of study:	Blind or partially sighted people, between twenty and thirty years of age, with or without other 'medical disabilities'. Some able to work and live independently, others not.
Coverage:	Small sample.
Timescale:	February 1989 - February 1990. 100 x 3-day weeks researcher time.
Cost:	Between £15,000 and £30,000.
Funding body/bodies:	Private sponsor.
Report(s):	A report of a qualitative nature will be published.

EMPLOYMENT SERVICES FOR THE VISUALLY HANDICAPPED: 'SIX-MONTH SURVEY'

Researcher(s):   Doug McCallum
Psychological Services Branch
Quality Standards and Methods Directorate
The Training Agency
General Office, Room N1008
Moorfoot, Sheffield S1 4PQ

[Note: Further changes within the Employment Department Group during 1990 led to the Training Agency (formerly Training Commission and previously Manpower Services Commission) being disbanded; its main functions are now located within the Training Enterprise and Education Directorate (TEED), based at Moorfoot, Sheffield.]

Abstract:

New service of employment advice being piloted in North West, East Midlands, and Eastern Regions from April 1988. Abolition of posts of Blind Persons' Resettlement Officer. Transfer of duties to the Disablement Resettlement Officer (DRO), with direct input from the RNIB. Disablement Advisory Service (DAS) team dealing only with retention cases and special employment. Based on recommendations of reports by Lomas for RNIB (1986).

Aims: To develop a model of good practice, using RNIB as a training and advisory service. To assess how clients and staff in two pilot regions judge the new approach.

Methods: Use of 'standards based approach' ... 'saying in advance what levels of performance would be expected of a good service, and then checking whether the service delivers this'. Feedback checks at 6-, 12- and 18-month points of the pilot. Collecting statistics. Field meetings with relevant staff. Postal survey to staff. Postal survey to visually impaired clients. (See also Summary of findings.)

Current status: 'Six-Month Survey' reported.

Summary of findings:

Standard chosen as 'satisfactory' is when 70 per cent or more respondents say that the service is operating 'adequately' or 'better than adequately'. Conversely, if 30 per cent or more identify a problem, this needs investigating further.

Response rates: DRO's in Regions identified - 89 per cent (91); DAS team members - 93 per cent (37); blind and partially sighted clients - 57 per cent (171).

Generally, staff were satisfied with the standard of service, their relationships with other agencies, and the training they had received for the new system. 77 per cent felt visually impaired clients required more time than their other clients. The majority initially failed to use the new action plans with clients. Clients expressed a slightly lower level of satisfaction in some areas: 'Overall satisfaction with the service received from the DRO related strongly to the amount of satisfaction expressed about the interview with the DRO' ... '*how* the service is being delivered rather than *what* is delivered ...' [emphases in original]. Service has not reached all potential clients yet. Attempt to explore other referral sources. Need to develop counselling services and reassess time allocated to this client group.

Subjects of study: See above.

Coverage: As above.

Timescale: Six months from April 1988.

Cost:

Funding body/bodies:

Report(s):   *Six-Month Report* published (1989) and obtainable from above address.

EMPLOYMENT SERVICES FOR THE VISUALLY HANDICAPPED: 'EIGHTEEN-MONTH SURVEY AND FINAL REPORT'

Researcher(s): Doug McCallum
Psychological Services Branch
Quality Standards and Methods Directorate
The Training Agency
General Office, Room N1008
Moorfoot, Sheffield S1 4PQ

[Note: Further changes within the Employment Department Group during 1990 led to the Training Agency (formerly Training Commission and previously Manpower Services Commission) being disbanded; its main functions are now located within the Training Enterprise and Education Directorate (TEED), based at Moorfoot, Sheffield.]

Abstract:

A continuation of the pilot project established in April 1988 (see entry [8(c)1]).

Methods: Repeat of postal questionnaires to staff and clients as outlined in entry [8(c)1] re. 'Six-Month Survey'. Continuation of meetings with staff and collection of statistics.

Current status: Completed.

Summary of findings:

Large increase in percentage of staff thinking referral system working well, but still reporting a lack of referrals and difficulties in getting BD8's from social services departments. Generally favourable reaction to DRO interviews and increase in use of action plans. Clients now more satisfied with their assessment and training courses from other services.

Subjects of study:	As per entry [8(c)1].
Coverage:	As per entry [8(c)1].
Timescale:	18 months from April 1988.
Cost:	
Funding body/bodies:	
Report(s):	*Eighteen-Month Survey and Final Report* published (1990) and obtainable from above address.

'A SENSE OF PURPOSE: A STUDY OF VISUALLY HANDICAPPED PEOPLE AND THEIR SEARCH FOR WORK'

Researcher(s): Jean Whaley
Social and Community Planning Research
35 Northampton Square
London EC1V 0AX
Tel: 0171 250 1866

Charles Mattison, Alison Dodd and Deborah Mullins
RNIB Employment Development Unit
Royal National Institute for the Blind
224 Great Portland Street
London W1N 6AA
Tel: 0171 388 1266

Abstract:

Approximately 40,000 of the 135,000 people registered as blind or partially sighted in England and Wales are of working age. RNIB Employment Development Unit wanted to look at needs and services re. those who wanted to work.

Aims: To obtain information on the experiences and views of visually impaired job seekers about the services aimed at helping them. To gain insight into the type of work sought. To relate these to the training and work experience of the job seekers.

Methods: Sample obtained from nine local authority registers; 318 eligible people interviewed.

Current status: Completed.

Summary of findings:

Nearly two-thirds of those interviewed were able to read and use residual vision; thirteen per cent were totally blind. Half had an additional health problem, but all felt able to go to unfamiliar places either accompanied or on their own. A majority expressed a preference for full-time work as an employee, rather than being self-employed. Choice of work reflected a wide range of interests and aptitudes unrelated to sight loss, but most common preferences were social services, education welfare and health, clerical work, and manufacturing. A higher proportion than the national average had no qualifications, and a higher proportion than the national average had been in higher education. Reasons for working included contact with others, to earn money, and to gain 'a sense of purpose'. There was a low level of knowledge of advisory services, especially those of RNIB. Forty-three per cent had contacted MSC. A need for counselling was expressed. RNIB sees a need for development work re. publicizing its services to potential clients, to potential employers and to relevant support agencies.

Subjects of study:	Registered blind or partially sighted men and women in England and Wales aged 16-59 who were seeking employment.
Coverage:	National sample, but authors feel it was limited by the way the Disabled Persons Register is kept by the MSC and by the 'dead wood' on SSD Registers.
Timescale:	
Cost:	
Funding body/bodies:	
Report(s):	RNIB Employment Development Unit (1986), *A Sense of Purpose: A Study of Visually Handicapped People and their Search for Work*, RNIB, London.

EMPLOYMENT REHABILITATION FEASIBILITY STUDIES
(One study covers England, Wales and Northern Ireland, with an identical study for Scotland)

Researcher(s):   Gillian Paschkes Bell and Zoe Wavell
Royal National Institute for the Blind
224 Great Portland Street
London W1N 6AA
Tel: 0171 388 1266

Abstract:

Aims: To consider the appropriate nature for RNIB's future employment rehabilitation service. Specific issues include the relationship between social rehabilitation, employment rehabilitation and training, and the involvement of families.

Methods: Interviews and questionnaires. Comparison with two overseas systems.

Current status: Draft report completed.

Summary of findings:

Draft Report: Clients would prefer a regionally distributed service, crossing the boundaries of social and employment rehabilitation, and including both residential and non-residential provision.

Subjects of study:	Present and past employment rehabilitation clients. Those working in employment rehabilitation. Spokespersons for organizations in related fields.
Coverage:	As above.
Timescale:	1 October 1989 - 31 July 1990.
Cost:	
Funding body/bodies:	RNIB.
Report(s):	Generally available towards the end of 1990.

VOCATIONAL OPPORTUNITIES FOR THE VISUALLY IMPAIRED WITH MANUAL AND ALLIED SKILLS

Researcher(s):   Philippa Simkiss
RNIB Employment Office
1 The Square
111 Broad Street
Birmingham B15 1AF
Tel: 0121 631 3372

Abstract:

Aims: To assess industrial trends generally and in a national context. To gain an understanding of the current situation of visually impaired manual workers. To gather data for a variety of occupations. To identify new opportunities within industry and the craft sector, and services suitable for manually skilled individuals.

Methods: Literature survey, with information from DE, CBI, EITB etc. Contact with individuals using RNIB and DE records. 'Mailshots' and interviews. Visits to places where visually impaired people work, investigating other processes/tasks on-site and the possibility of training a visually impaired person to carry them out.

Current status: Data collection and analysis for Stage 1 (industrial trend assessment).

Summary of findings:

Subjects of study:	Anyone with a visual impairment (not necessarily registered).
Coverage:	National in sense outlined above.
Timescale:	1 April 1990 - 31 March 1992. 1 full-time and 1 part-time researcher at present.
Cost:	
Funding body/bodies:	
Report(s):	Will be published (including interim reports).

Index of organizations with research listed

Academic institutions and independent research bodies

National Foundation for Educational Research (NFER)

'Beyond Vision: Training for Workers in Visual Impairment' [4(c)7, p. 217]

University of Birmingham, Research Centre for the Education of the Visually Handicapped, School of Education (RCEVH)

Access to Information and Learning by Visually Handicapped People Through Micro-Computer Technology [4(o)1, p. 219]

The Elders Project: A Longitudinal Enquiry [1B(o)1, p. 159]

The Manual Dexterity of Visually Handicapped Adults [4(c)5, p. 213]

Using Sighted Volunteers for Teaching Moon to Newly Blinded Adults [4(o)4, p. 225]

University of Manchester, Hester Adrian Research Centre

Evaluation of SENSE Midlands (Further Education) [5(o)2, p. 237]

University of Nottingham, Blind Mobility Research Unit, Department of Psychology (BMRU)

The Development of Measures of Low Vision Mobility Performance [2(c)1,

p. 175]

Evaluation of Assessment Procedures at the RNIB Rehabilitation Centre, Torquay [4(c)1, p. 205]

Gait Analysis [3(c)1, p. 183]

Identification of Potential Confusions in Lesson Analysis Schedule [4(c)2, p. 207]

Investigation of Mobility Officers' Assessments of Clients' Needs for Training [4(c)3, p. 209]

Investigation of Mobility Related Feelings [3(c)2, p. 185]

Low Vision Assessment and Training [4(c)4, p. 211]

Mobility Related Feelings and the Walking Speed of Visually Impaired Travellers [3(o)2, p. 193]

Motion Vision in the Partially Sighted [2(o)2, p. 181]

Obstacle Location Without Vision [3(o)3, p. 195]

Preliminary Comparison of Expert and Poor Travellers' Abilities to Cope with Independent Travel [3(o)4, p. 197]

Psychological Adjustment to Sight Loss [4(o)3, p. 223]

Role-Play of Different Training Styles [4(c)6, p. 215]

The 'Sonic Pathfinder' [3(c)3, p. 187]

Spatial Representation and Congenital Blindness [3(c)4, p. 189]

Task Analysis of Mobility [3(o)5, p. 199]

Visual Balance Control [3(o)7, p. 203]

University of Sheffield, Department of Psychology

Use of Maps and Graphics in the Mobility Training of Young Visually Handicapped Children [3(o)6, p. 201]

Statutory agencies (mainly social services departments)

Bedfordshire Joint Care Planning Team

Strategic Framework 1991-2001 [1A(o)3, p. 151]

London Borough of Bexley, Directorate of Housing and Personal Services

Review of Services for Hearing Impaired and Visually Handicapped People

271

Visually Disabled Services in Tameside [1A(c)7, p. 143]

The Training Agency, Psychological Services Branch

Employment Services for the Visually Handicapped: 'Six-Month Survey' [8(c)1, p. 259]

Employment Services for the Visually Handicapped: 'Eighteen-Month Survey and Final Report' [8(c)2, p. 261]

Westminster City Council, Social Services Department

Services for People with Disabilities [1A(c)5, p. 139]

Voluntary organizations

Brighton Society for the Blind

Evaluation Study of an Adviser/Counsellor Based at an Eye Hospital [1C(o)1, p. 173]

Bristol Royal Society for the Blind

Day Care for Visually Impaired People with Learning Difficulties [6(c)1, p. 245]

Deaf-Blind Services in Avon [5(o)1, p. 235]

Low Vision Services in Avon, *(with Avon County Council, Social Services Department)* [2(o)1, p. 179]

Mobility Aids for Visually Impaired People [3(o)1, p. 191]

Prevention of Blindness: An Examination of Changing Patterns of Care and the Impact on Sight Loss [1B(o)3, p. 163]

The Registration and Continuing Care of People with a Visual Impairment *(with Avon County Council, Social Services Department)* [1A(c)4, p. 137]

Transport Facilities for the Visually Impaired in Bristol, *Bristol Royal Society for the Blind* [1B(c)2, p. 155]

Visual Assessment at the Wyvern Special Education Centre, Pewsey [6(c)4, p. 251]

Cambridgeshire Society for the Blind and Partially Sighted

Survey of Needs: Visually Impaired People of Cambridgeshire [1B(o)5, p. 167]

Chester Blind Welfare Society

Comparison of Education Facilities for Visually Impaired Youngsters in Clywd and Cheshire [7(c)1, p. 255]

Survey of Needs of Visually Impaired People Within the Ten Districts Covered by the Chester Blind Welfare Society [1B(o)6, p. 169]

Deaf-Blind Services Liaison Group (RNIB, NDBL, SENSE, RNID)

'Breaking Through: Developing Services for Deaf-Blind People' [5(c)1, p. 229]

Sight Concern Hampshire, Hampshire Association for the Care of the Blind

Visually Handicapped People in Hampshire: A Survey of Needs [1B(c)3, p. 157]

Impact Foundation/Worthing District Health Authority

'Operation Cataract': Operations on a Day Care Basis with Hotel After-Care, [1C(c)1, p. 171]

The Partially Sighted Society

'The Client's View: Social and Rehabilitation Services' [1B(c)1, p. 153]

Evaluation of a Low Vision Training Programme [4(o)2, p. 221]

Evaluation of Task Lighting [2(c)2, p. 177]

Royal London Society for the Blind

Further Education Needs, Academic and Social, of the Blind and Partially Sighted [7(o)1, p. 257]

Royal National Institute for the Blind (RNIB)

Employment Rehabilitation Feasibility Studies [8(o)1, p. 265]

General Needs Survey [1B(o)2, p. 161]

Local Authority Social Rehabilitation Services to Visually Handicapped People ('The Shore Report') [1A(c)3, p. 135]

'Out of Isolation: A Plan for the Growth of Services to Multi-Handicapped Visually Impaired People' [6(c)3, p. 249]

'A Sense of Purpose: A Study of Visually Handicapped People and their Search for Work' [8(c)3, p. 263]

Vocational Opportunities for the Visually Impaired with Manual and

Allied Skills [8(o)2, p. 267]

'Working Together: The Scope for Improving Working Links between RNIB and Local Societies for the Blind' [1A(c)8, p. 145]

South Regional Association for the Blind (SRAB)

Services for Multi-Handicapped Visually Impaired People [6(o)1, p. 253]

Sunderland and Durham County Incorporated Royal Institution for the Blind

Provision of Services for Deaf-Blind People [5(o)4, p. 241]

Surrey Voluntary Association for the Blind

Welfare of the Visually Impaired: Daily Living Skills and Independence [4(o)5, p. 227]

Index of titles of research projects listed

275

Day Care for Visually Impaired People with Learning Difficulties, *Bristol Royal Society for the Blind* [6(c)1, p. 245]

Deaf-Blind Services in Avon, *Bristol Royal Society for the Blind* [5(o)1, p. 235]

The Development of Measures of Low Vision Mobility Performance, *Blind Mobility Research Unit, University of Nottingham* [2(c)1, p. 175]

The Elders Project: A Longitudinal Enquiry, *Research Centre for the Education of the Visually Handicapped* [1B(o)1, p. 159]

Employment Rehabilitation Feasibility Studies, *RNIB* [8(o)1, p. 265]

Employment Services for the Visually Handicapped: 'Six-Month Survey', *Psychological Services Branch, The Training Agency* [8(c)1, p. 259]

Employment Services for the Visually Handicapped: 'Eighteen-Month Survey and Final Report', *Psychological Services Branch, The Training Agency* [8(c)2, p. 261]

Evaluation of Assessment Procedures at the RNIB Rehabilitation Centre, Torquay, *Blind Mobility Research Unit* [4(c)1, p. 205]

Evaluation of a Low Vision Training Programme, *Partially Sighted Society* [4(o)2, p. 221]

Evaluation of SENSE Midlands (Further Education), *Hester Adrian Research Centre, University of Manchester* [5(o)2, p. 237]

Evaluation Study of an Adviser/Counsellor Based at an Eye Hospital, *Brighton Society for the Blind* [1C(o)1, p. 173]

Evaluation of Task Lighting, *Partially Sighted Society* [2(c)2, p. 177]

Feasibility Study for a County-Wide Service for Deaf-Blind People, *Social Services Department, Norfolk County Council* [5(c)2, p. 231]

Further Education Needs, Academic and Social, of the Blind and Partially Sighted, *Royal London Society for the Blind* [7(o)1, p. 257]

Gait Analysis, *Blind Mobility Research Unit* [3(c)1, p. 183]

General Needs Survey, *RNIB* [1B(o)2, p. 161]

Identification of Potential Confusions in Lesson Analysis Schedule, *Blind*

Mobility Research Unit [4(c)2, p. 207]

Identifying Needs and Numbers of Deaf-Blind In Devon, *Social Services Department, Devon County Council/SENSE South West* [5(o)3, p. 239]

Investigation of Mobility Officers' Assessments of Clients' Needs for Training, *Blind Mobility Research Unit* [4(c)3, p. 209]

Investigation of Mobility Related Feelings, *Blind Mobility Research Unit* [3(c)2, p. 185]

Local Authority Social Rehabilitation Services to Visually Handicapped People ('The Shore Report'), *RNIB* [1A(c)3, p. 135]

Low Vision Assessment and Training, *Blind Mobility Research Unit* [4(c)4, p. 211]

Low Vision Services in Avon, *Bristol Royal Society for the Blind/Social Services Department, Avon County Council* [2(o)1, p. 179]

The Manual Dexterity of Visually Handicapped Adults, *Research Centre for the Education of the Visually Handicapped* [4(c)5, p. 213]

Mentally Handicapped People with Hearing and Sight Problems, *Social Services Department, Cornwall County Council* [6(c)2, p. 247]

Mobility Aids for Visually Impaired People, *Bristol Royal Society for the Blind* [3(o)1, p. 191]

Mobility Related Feelings and the Walking Speed of Visually Impaired Travellers, *Blind Mobility Research Unit* [3(o)2, p. 193]

Motion Vision in the Partially Sighted, *Blind Mobility Research Unit* [2(o)2, p. 181]

Obstacle Location Without Vision, *Blind Mobility Research Unit* [3(o)3, p. 195]

'Operation Cataract': Operations on a Day Care Basis with Hotel After-Care, *Impact Foundation/Worthing District Health Authority* [1C(c)1, p. 171]

'Out of Isolation: A Plan for the Growth of Services to Multi-Handicapped Visually Impaired People', *RNIB* [6(c)3, p. 249]

Preliminary Comparison of Expert and Poor Travellers' Abilities to Cope with Independent Travel, *Blind Mobility Research Unit* [3(o)4, p. 197]

Prevention of Blindness: An Examination of Changing Patterns of Care and the Impact on Sight Loss, *Bristol Royal Society for the Blind* [1B(o)3, p. 163]

Provision of Services for Deaf-Blind People, *Sunderland and Durham County Incorporated Royal Institution for the Blind* [5(o)4, p. 241]

Psychological Adjustment to Sight Loss, *Blind Mobility Research Unit* [4(o)3, p. 223]

The Registration and Continuing Care of People with a Visual Impairment, *Bristol Royal Society for the Blind/Social Services Department, Avon County Council* [1A(c)4, p. 137]

Review of Services for Hearing Impaired and Visually Handicapped People, *Directorate of Housing and Personal Services, London Borough of Bexley* [5(c)3, p. 233]

Review of Services for People with a Visual Disability, *Social Services Department, Buckinghamshire County Council* [1A(o)2, p. 149]

Review and Survey of the Provision of Services to People who are Deaf-Blind, *Social Services Division, Stockport Metropolitan Borough Council* [5(o)5, p. 243]

Role-Play of Different Training Styles, *Blind Mobility Research Unit* [4(c)6, p. 215]

'A Sense of Purpose: A Study of Visually Handicapped People and their Search for Work', *RNIB* [8(c)3, p. 263]

Services for Multi-Handicapped Visually Impaired People, *SRAB* [6(o)1, p. 253]

Services for People with Disabilities, *Social Services Department, Westminster City Council* [1A(c)5, p. 139]

Services for People with a Visual Impairment, *South Devon Review and Planning Group/Partially Sighted Society* [1A(c)6, p. 141]

The 'Sonic Pathfinder', *Blind Mobility Research Unit* [3(c)3, p. 187]

Spatial Representation and Congenital Blindness, *Blind Mobility Research Unit* [3(c)4, p. 189]

Strategic Framework 1991-2001, *Bedfordshire Joint Care Planning Team* [1A(o)3, p. 151]

Survey and Review of Needs, *Department of Social Services and Housing, London Borough of Bromley/Kent Association for the Blind* [1B(o)4, p. 165]

Survey of Needs: Visually Impaired People of Cambridgeshire, *Cambridgeshire Society for the Blind and Partially Sighted* [1B(o)5, p. 167]

Survey of Needs of Visually Impaired People Within the Ten Districts Covered by the Chester Blind Welfare Society, *Chester Blind Welfare Society* [1B(o)6, p. 169]

Task Analysis of Mobility, *Blind Mobility Research Unit* [3(o)5, p. 199]

Transport Facilities for the Visually Impaired in Bristol, *Bristol Royal Society for the Blind* [1B(c)2, p. 155]

Use of Maps and Graphics in the Mobility Training of Young Visually Handicapped Children, *Department of Psychology, University of Sheffield* [3(o)6, p. 201]

Using Sighted Volunteers for Teaching Moon to Newly Blinded Adults, *Research Centre for the Education of the Visually Handicapped* [4(o)4, p. 225]

Visual Assessment at the Wyvern Special Education Centre, Pewsey, *Bristol Royal Society for the Blind* [6(c)4, p. 251]

Visual Balance Control, *Blind Mobility Research Unit* [3(o)7, p. 203]

Visually Disabled Services in Tameside, *Social Services Department, Tameside Metropolitan Borough Council/RNIB* [1A(c)7, p. 143]

Visually Handicapped People in Hampshire: A Survey of Needs, *Sight Concern Hampshire, Hampshire Association for the Care of the Blind* [1B(c)3, p. 157]

Vocational Opportunities for the Visually Impaired with Manual and Allied Skills, *RNIB* [8(o)2, p. 267]

Welfare of the Visually Impaired: Daily Living Skills and Independence, *Surrey Voluntary Association for the Blind* [4(o)5, p. 227]

'Working Together: The Scope for Improving Working Links between RNIB and Local Societies for the Blind', *RNIB* [1A(c)8, p. 145]

References

Abberley, P. (1991), 'The Significance of the OPCS Disability Surveys', in Oliver, M. (ed.), *op. cit.*, pp. 156-176.

Abberley, P. (1992), 'Counting us out: a discussion of the OPCS disability surveys', *Disability, Handicap & Society, (Special Issue: Researching Disability)*, vol. 7, no. 2., pp. 139-55.

Abel, R.A.D. (1987), *Identification of the Blind, 1834-1968: A Study of the Establishment of the Blind Register and the Registration Process*, unpublished PhD Thesis, University of London.

Abel, R.A. (1989), 'Visually impaired people, the identification of the need for specialist provision: a historical perspective', *British Journal of Visual Impairment*, vol. 7, no. 2, pp. 47-51.

d'Aboville, E. (1991), 'Social Work in an Organisation of Disabled People', in Oliver, M. (ed.), *op. cit.*, pp. 64-85.

The Audit Commission for Local Authorities and the National Health Service in England and Wales (1992), *The Community Revolution: Personal Social Services and Community Care* (Audit Commission Report No. 8), HMSO, London.

Beardshaw, V. (1988), *Last on the List: Community Services for People with Physical Disabilities*, Research Report 3, King's Fund Institute, London.

Beggs, W.D.A. (1985), 'Giving blind people access to the world', *Social Work Today*, 14 October, pp. 14-23.

Beggs, W.D.A. (1989a), 'Empathy in assessment and training', in Blind Mobility Research Unit, *op. cit.*, 10.

Beggs, W.D.A. (1989b), 'Mobility related feelings and skill level', in Blind

Mobility Research Unit, *op. cit.*, 7.

Beresford, P. and Croft, S. (1986), *Whose Welfare: Private Care or Public Services?*, Lewis Cohen Urban Studies Centre, Brighton.

Beresford, P. and Croft, S. (1990), *From Paternalism to Participation: Involving People in Social Services*, Open Services Project/Joseph Rowntree Foundation, London.

Best, A.B., Ennals, P. and Johnson, P. (1987), *Out of Isolation: A Plan for the Growth of Services to Multi-Handicapped Visually Impaired People*, RNIB, London.

Bewley, C, and Glendinning, C. (1994) *Involving Disabled People in Community Care Planning*, Joseph Rowntree Foundation, York.

Blind Mobility Research Unit (1989), *Update and Future Proposals on Research Programme, January 1989-December 1990*, BMRU Report No. 216, Department of Psychology, University of Nottingham, Nottingham.

British Journal of Visual Impairment (1992), Editorial, 'Community Care: its significance for visually impaired people?', *British Journal of Visual Impairment*, vol. 10, no. 3, pp. 77-8.

Bruce, I. and McKennell, A. (1986), 'RNIB General Needs Survey', *New Beacon*, vol. 70, no. 830, pp. 165-8.

Bruce, I., McKennell, A. and Walker, E. (1991), *Blind and Partially Sighted Adults in Britain: The RNIB Survey, Volume 1*, HMSO, London.

Calnan, S.E. (1981), *Elderly People with Poor Sight at Home*, unpublished research report, Department of Environmental and Preventive Medicine, St Bartholomew's Hospital Medical College, London.

Central Council for Education and Training in Social Work (1993), *Back from the Wellhouse: Discussion Papers on Sensory Impairment and Training in Community Care*, CCETSW Paper 32.1, CCETSW, London.

Central Statistical Office (1990), *Social Trends 20*, HMSO, London.

Challis, L. (1991), 'Quality assurance in social services departments - new wine in old bottles?', *Research, Policy and Planning*, vol. 9, no. 1, pp. 17-19.

Clark-Carter, D.D., Howarth, C.I., Heyes, A.D., Dodds, A.G. and Armstrong, J.D. (1981), *The Visually Handicapped in the City of Nottingham: A survey of their disabilities, mobility, employment, and daily living skills*, BMRU Report No. 69, Department of Psychology, University of Nottingham, Nottingham.

Clarke, T., M.P., (1991), 'Developing community care: A Parliamentary view', in Ulas, M., Black, S. and Hambledon, P. (eds) *Community Care - A Mixed Economy? Papers from a SSRG Workshop*, Social Services Research Group, Manchester, pp. 29-32.

Collins, J. (1987), 'Coping with the rising incidence of partial sight', *Optometry Today*, 5 December.

Cullinan, T.R. (1977), *The Epidemiology of Visual Disability: Studies of Visually Disabled People in the Community*, Health Services Research Unit Report No. 28, University of Kent, Canterbury.

Cullinan, T.R. and Silver, J. (1986), *Visual Disability in the Elderly*, Croom

Helm, London.

DHSS (1968), *Report of the Committee on Local Authority and Allied Personal Social Services*, Cmnd 3703, HMSO, London. ('The Seebohm Report'.)

DHSS (1981), *Care in Action: A Handbook of Policies and Priorities for the Health and Personal Social Services in England*, HMSO, London.

DHSS (1987a), *Local Authority Social Services Statistics: Staff of Local Authority Social Services Departments at 30 September 1985, England*, DHSS, London.

DHSS (1987b), *Promoting Better Health: The Government's Programme for Improving Primary Health Care*, (White Paper) Cm 249, HMSO, London.

DHSS (SSI) (1988a), *Say it Again: Inspection of Contemporary Social Work Practice with People who are Deaf or Hard of Hearing*, DHSS, London.

DHSS (SSI) (1988b), *A Wider Vision: The Management and Organisation of Services for People who are Blind or Visually Handicapped*, DHSS, London.

DoH (1989a), *Caring for People: Community Care in the Next Decade and Beyond*, (White Paper) Cm 849, HMSO, London.

DoH (1989b), *Co-ordinating Services for Visually Handicapped People: Report to the Minister for the Disabled*, HMSO, London.

DoH (1989c), *Working for Patients - The Health Service: Caring for the 1990s*, (White Paper) Cm 555, HMSO, London.

DoH (1990), *Community Care in the Next Decade and Beyond: Policy Guidance*, HMSO, London.

DoH (1994), *A Wider Strategy for Research and Development Relating to Personal Social Services. Report to the Director of Research and Development, Department of Health, by an Independent Review Group*, HMSO, London.

DoH (SSI) (1989), *Sign Posts: Leading to Better Social Services for Deaf-Blind People*, DoH, London.

DoH (SSI) (1991a), *Assessment Systems and Community Care*, SSI, London.

DoH (SSI) (1991b), *Good Sense Guide*, DoH, London.

DoH (SSI) (1993), *"Whose Life is it, Anyway?" A report of an inspection of services for people with multiple impairments*, DoH, London.

DoH (SSI)/Scottish Office (SWSG) (1991), *Care Management and Assessment: Summary of Practice Guidance; Practitioners' Guide; and Managers' Guide* (three publications), HMSO, London.

DoH (SSI/NHSME) (1993a), *Assessment Special Study: A Joint SSI/NHSME Study of Assessment Procedures in Five Local Authority Areas*, DoH, London.

DoH (SSI/NHSME) (1993b), *Implementing Community Care for Younger People with Physical and Sensory Disabilities: Report and Findings of the SSI/NHSME Special Project*, DoH, London.

Disability, Handicap & Society (1992), *Special Issue: Researching Disability*, vol. 7, no. 2.

Dodds, A.G. (1985), 'Multi-handicap, low vision and the teaching of mobility', *British Journal of Visual Impairment*, vol. 3, no. 2, pp. 38-40.

Dodds, A.G. (1988), *Mobility Training for Visually Handicapped People: A Person-Centred Approach*, Croom Helm, London.

Dodds, A.G. (1989), 'Motivation reconsidered: the importance of self-efficacy in rehabilitation', *British Journal of Visual Impairment*, vol. 7, no. 1, pp. 11-15.

Dodds, A.G., Gaskell, A.P.D. and Hellawell, D.J. (1989), 'Adjustment, intervention and rehabilitation outcomes', in Blind Mobility Research Unit, *op. cit.*, 1.

Dodds, A.G. and Hellawell, D.J. (1989), 'Auditory awareness training', in Blind Mobility Research Unit, *op. cit.*, 5.

Ellis, K. (1993), *Squaring the Circle: User and Carer Participation in Needs Assessment*, Joseph Rowntree Foundation, York.

Finkelstein, V. (1985), Paper given at World Health Organisation Meeting, 24-28 June, Netherlands. (Quoted in Oliver, M. (1990), *op. cit.*, p. 6.)

Finkelstein, V. (1991), 'Disability: An Administrative Challenge? (The Health and Welfare Heritage), in Oliver, M. (ed.), *op. cit.*, pp. 19-39.

Ford, M. and Henshel, T., with Theakstone, A. (1994), *The In Touch 1994/5 Handbook*, Broadcasting Support Services (for the BBC), London.

Goldberg, E.M. and Connelly, N. (1982), *The Effectiveness of Social Care for the Elderly*, Policy Studies Institute/Heinemann, London.

Griffiths, R. (1988), *Community Care: Agenda for Action - a Report to the Secretary of State for Social Services by Sir Roy Griffiths*, HMSO, London. ('The (second) Griffiths Report'.)

Hardy, B., Wistow, G. and Leedham, I. (1993), *Analysis of a Sample of English Community Care Plans 1993/94*, DoH, London. (One of the first six reports published from a series of fourteen Special Studies undertaken or commissioned by the Social Services Inspectorate and NHS Management Executive to monitor the implementation of *Caring for People*. (See also refs DoH (SSI/NHSME), 1993a, 1993b.)

Harries, U., Leventhall, R. and Popay, J. (1992), *Assessing the Health and Social Care Needs of Visually Disabled Older People: An interim project report*, Research Report 1, Public Health Research and Resource Centre, Salford.

Harris, A. (1971), *Handicapped and Impaired in Great Britain*, HMSO, London.

Hill, A.R., Aspinall, P.A. and Greenwood, R. (1992), 'Information used in rehabilitation decisions: some research results', *British Journal of Visual Impairment*, vol. 10, no. 3, pp. 83-7.

Hutchinson, L. (1993), *The Salford Eye Care Project*, Henshaw's Society for the Blind, Manchester.

Insight Management Consulting (1994), *Review of the Effectiveness of Form BD8 Procedures*, London, DoH.

James, P. (1993), 'Insight on sight loss', *Community Care*, 5 August, pp. 24-5.

Leventhall, R. (1992), *A Review of the Literature on Visual Impairment and Disability Among Older People in Britain: A case study in epidemiologically based needs assessment*, Occasional Paper 1, Public Health Research and Resource Centre, Salford.

Lomas, G.M. (1986a), *Education and Training for Work: Report Three. The support needed by visually handicapped people in preparing for the world of work*, RNIB, London.

Lomas, G.M. (1986b), *Employment Trends and the Visually Handicapped: Report One. The changing work scene and its impact on jobs*, RNIB, London.

Lomas, G.M. (1986c), *Finding Work: Report Two. A review of placement services for visually handicapped people*, RNIB, London.

Lomas, G. and Vaughan, H. (1987), *Working Together: The Scope for Improving Working Links between RNIB and Local Societies for the Blind*, RNIB, London.

Lovelock, R. and Edge, S. (1991), *Research Review: Services For and Social Care of Blind and Partially Sighted People. Report to the Department of Health*, CEDR, Department of Social Work Studies, University of Southampton, Southampton.

Lovelock, R. and Powell, J. (1994), *Disability: Britain in Europe. An evaluation of UK participation in the HELIOS programme (1988-1991)*, Avebury, Aldershot.

Marsh, P. and Fisher, M. (1992), *Good Intentions: Developing Partnerships in Social Services*, Joseph Rowntree Foundation, York.

Maychell, K. and Smart, D. (1990), *Beyond Vision: Training for Workers in Visual Impairment*, NFER/Nelson, London.

Morris, J. (1993), *Community Care or Independent Living?*, Joseph Rowntree Foundation, York.

Moss, J. (1985), *Third Demographic Study - visually handicapped people with additional disabilities: England*, RNIB, London.

Neslen, H. (1989), 'Providing for old age', *New Beacon*, vol. 73, no. 862, pp. 73-7.

Office of Population Censuses and Surveys (1988 and 1989), *OPCS Surveys of Disability in Great Britain*, HMSO, London.

Report 1. Martin, J., Meltzer, H. and Elliot, D. (1988), *The prevalence of disability among adults*.

Report 2. Martin, J. and White, A. (1988), *The financial circumstances of disabled adults living in private households*.

Report 3. Bone, M. and Meltzer, H. (1989), *The prevalence of disability among children*.

Report 4. Martin, J., White, A. and Meltzer, H. (1989), *Disabled adults: services, transport and employment*.

Report 5. Smyth, M. and Robus, N. (1989), *The financial circumstances of families with disabled children living in private households*.

Report 6. Meltzer, H., Smyth, M. and Robus, N. (1989), *Disabled children: services, transport and education*.

Oliver, M. (1987), 'Re-defining disability: a challenge to research', *Research, Policy and Planning*, vol. 5, no. 1, pp. 9-13.

Oliver, M. (1990), *The Politics of Disablement*, Macmillan, Basingstoke.

Oliver, M. (ed.) (1991), *Social Work: Disabled People and Disabling Environments. Research Highlights in Social Work 21*, Jessica Kingsley Publishers, London.

Phelan, P. (1984), 'Are we producing the goods?', *British Journal of Visual*

Impairment, vol. 2, no. 3, pp. 70-3.

Robbins, D. (ed.) (1993), *Community Care: Findings from Department of Health Funded Research 1988-1992*, HMSO, London.

Rogers, E.M. (1983), *Diffusion of Innovations*, (3rd edition), Free Press, New York.

Ross, J.E. (1985), 'Visual disability amongst the elderly', *British Journal of Visual Impairment*, vol. 3, no. 2, pp. 45-7.

Royal National Institute for the Blind (Employment Development Unit) (1986), *A Sense of Purpose: A Study of Visually Handicapped People and their Search for Work*, RNIB, London.

Royal National Institute for the Blind (1987a), *Directory of Agencies for the Blind in the British Isles and Overseas*, (Interim edition), RNIB, London.

Royal National Institute for the Blind (1987b), *Meeting the Needs of Visually Handicapped People: RNIB Aims and Strategy*, RNIB, London.

Royal National Institute for the Blind (Deaf-Blind Services Liaison Group) (1988), *Breaking Through: Developing Services for Deaf-Blind People*, RNIB, London.

Royal National Institute for the Blind (Social Services Development Unit) (1994), *Reaching the Needs of People with Visual Disabilities*, (Training Package), HMSO, London.

Rumney, N. (1992), 'An optometric approach to low vision services', *British Journal of Visual Impairment*, vol. 10, no. 3, pp. 89-92.

Sapey, B. and Hewitt, N. (1991), 'The Changing Context of Social Work Practice', in Oliver, M. (ed.), *op. cit.*, pp. 40-54.

Shankland Cox Partnerships (1985a), *Initial Demographic Study - A review of available data on the visually disabled population*, RNIB, London.

Shankland Cox Partnerships (1985b), *Second Demographic Study - Visually impaired children: England*, RNIB, London.

Shaw, J. (1985), 'The registration of blind and partially sighted people: an appraisal of the scheme in a southern county of England', *Social Services Research*, vol. 14, no. 5, pp. 67-86.

Shore, P. (1985), *Local Authority Social Rehabilitation Services to Visually Handicapped People*, RNIB, London. ('The Shore Report'.)

Smale, G., Domoney, L., Tuson, G., Ahmad, B., Sainsbury, E. and Darvill, G. (1994), *Negotiating Care in the Community*, HMSO, London.

Smale, G. and Tuson, G., with Biehal, N. and Marsh, P. (1993), *Empowerment, Assessment, Care Management and the Skilled Worker*, HMSO, London.

Stevens, A. (1993), 'Introduction' to CCETSW, *op. cit.*, pp. 9-11.

Stevenson, O. (1992), Review of The Audit Commission (1992), op. cit., *British Journal of Visual Impairment*, vol. 10, no. 3, pp. 109-10.

Stocking, B. (1985), *Initiative and Inertia: Case Studies in the NHS*, Nuffield Provincial Hospitals Trust, London.

Sutton, D. (1991), 'A betrayal of trust', *Community Care*, 23 May, p. 7.

Thomas, D. (1991), 'The relevance of certification, registration and assessment for people with a visual impairment', *British Journal of Visual Impairment*, vol. 9, no. 2, pp. 35-7.

Tobin, M.J. (1984), 'Future Research in the Field of Visual Handicap', (Address to the Annual Delegate Conference of the National Federation of the Blind of the UK, Edinburgh, August, 1983), *New Beacon*, vol. 68, no. 805, pp. 117-120.

Tobin, M.J. (1987), 'Special and mainstream schooling: some teenagers' views', *New Beacon*, vol. 71, no. 837, pp. 3-6.

Tobin, M.J. and Hill, E. (1984), 'Blind in Birmingham: a pilot survey of needs and of knowledge of available services', *New Beacon*, vol 68, no. 803, pp. 61-6.

Tobin, M.J. and Hill, E.W. (1988), 'Visually impaired teenagers: ambitions, attitudes and interests', *Journal of Visual Impairment and Blindness*, vol. 82, no. 12, pp. 414-16.

Tobin, M.J. and Hill, E.W. (1989), 'The present and the future: concerns of visually impaired teenagers', *British Journal of Visual Impairment*, vol. 7, no. 2, pp. 55-7.

UPIAS (1976), 'Fundamental Principles of Disability', Union of the Physically Impaired Against Segregation, London. (Quoted in Oliver, M. (1990), *op. cit.*, p. 11.)

Walker, E., Tobin, M. and McKennell, A. (1992), *Blind and Partially Sighted Children in Britain: The RNIB Survey, Volume 2*, HMSO, London.

Welsh Office (SSI) (1991), *Services for People with Visual Impairment in Gwynedd: Report of an Inspection May/June 1991*, Welsh Office (SSI), Cardiff.

Williams, G., with Hutchinson, L. et al. (1992), *Locked in a World of Your Own: The Needs of Older People with Vision Problems. A Report to the Department of Public Health, Salford Health Authority*, Department of Sociology, University of Salford, Salford.

Williams, P.C. (1993), 'Care management and assessment with blind and partially sighted people', in CCETSW, *op. cit.*, pp. 39-91.

Wistow, G (1990), *Community Care Planning: A Review of Past Experience and Future Imperatives*, Caring for People Implementation Document, CCI3, DoH, London.

Wistow, G. (1991), 'Quality and research: the policy and legislative context', *Research, Policy and Planning*, vol. 9, no. 1, pp. 9-12.

Wistow, G., Leedham, I. and Hardy, B. (1993), *Implementing Community Care: Preliminary Analysis of a Sample of English Community Care Plans*, DoH, London.

Wood, P.N.H. (1980), 'The language of disablement: a glossary relating to disease and its consequences', *International Rehabilitation Medicine*, vol. 2, pp. 86-92.

World Health Organisation (1981), *International Classification of Impairments, Disabilities and Handicaps*, WHO, Geneva.